DICTIONARY FOR THE ELECTRICIAN
WITH FORMULAS

By Tom Henry

While every precaution has been taken in the preparation of this course to ensure accuracy and reliability of the information, instructions, and directions, it is in no way to be construed as a guarantee. The author and publisher assumes no responsibility for errors or omissions. Neither is any liability assumed from the use of the information contained herein in case of misinterpretations, human error, or typographical errors.

National Electrical Code® and NEC® are Registered Trademarks of the National Fire Protection Association, Inc., Quincy, MA.

ISBN   0-945495-55-2

Someone once asked Einstein how many feet are in a mile. "I don't know", Einstein is reported as saying. "Why should I fill my head with things like that when I could look them up in any reference book in two minutes?"

NIKOLA TESLA

July 10, 1856 - January 7, 1943

"The AC man that lit up the world."

Since we never learned about him in school and all the textbooks give Edison the credit, I wanted to dedicate this page of my book to Nikola Tesla since the world turns today due to his inventions.

An eccentric scientist and inventor from Yugoslavia, Tesla came to New York in 1884 with a childhood dream to harness the power of Niagara Falls which he did on November 16, 1896.

At St. Louis in 1893 Tesla made the first public demonstration of Radio, although Marconi is credited with this achievement in 1895.

Among his many inventions Tesla developed the induction motor, complete polyphase AC system, split-phase motor, pushed for and established a standard 60 cycle system, and the Tesla coil which is used in every radio and TV.

Tesla was so far ahead of his time that the best of them mistook him for a dreamer. If there ever was a man who created so much and whose praises were sung so little, it was Nikola Tesla.

"Let the future tell the truth and evaluate each one according to his work and accomplishment. The present is theirs, the future, for which I really worked, is mine". *Tesla.*

" a book for an electrician by an electrician"…

CONTENTS

Ambient Temperatures 330
Area of Square Inch 328
Bus Bar Ampacity 327
Circle 326
Circumference 326
Cross-sectional area 326
Conductor,
   Insulation Damage 329
Conduit,
   Fitting Dimensions 337
Conversion Table 355
Degrees, elect.-mechanical . 347
Diameter 326
Dictionary 1
Drill Bit - Tap Sizes 336
Fire Facts 317
Fire Glossary 321
Formulas 324
Ignition Temperatures 319
Melting Point Of Metals 330
Metric Measurements 332

Motor,
   Capacitor Start 339
   DC Motor Reversing 341
   Rotor - Stator 344
   Synchronous 343
   Three ø Connections 345
   Three ø Reversing 342
   Wound - Rotor 341
Open - Delta 354
Power Wheel 325
Pronunciation 310
Short - Circuit Ratings 329
Square Mils 327
Temperature Conversion 335
Thermometer Scale 334
Transformer,
   Auto 351
   Connections 348
   Current 352
   Open Delta 354
   Voltage 353
Weights - Measurements 331

DICTIONARY

A

absorption. The property of materials such as clothing, drapes, carpeting on racks, acoustic ceilings, etc., which causes them to soak up or deaden sound.

AC adapter. A device intended to convert line voltage alternating current to low voltage AC or DC current.

accent lighting. Directional lighting to emphasize an object or draw attention to a part of the field of view.

accessible (readily). Capable of being reached quickly for operation, renewal, or inspections, without damaging the building structure or finish, or not permanently closed in by the structure or finish of the building.

accessible (wiring methods). Capable of being removed or exposed without damaging the building structure or finish, or not permanently closed in by the structure or finish of the building.

accessories. Devices that perform a secondary or minor duty as a refinement to the primary duty of the equipment.

accumulator. A European name for a rechargeable storage battery.

acoustics. The aliveness of deadness of sound in a room.

acute angle. An angle less than 90°, or less than a right angle.

adapter. A device for connecting parts that will not mate.

adjustable resistor. A resistor so constructed that its resistance can be changed by moving and setting one or more movable contacts.

adjustable-speed motor. A motor, the speed of which can be varied gradually over a considerable range.

admittance. The apparent conducting power of an alternating current circuit; the reciprocal of the impedance. The measure of ease with which an alternating current flows in a circuit.

aerial cable. An assembly of insulated conductors installed on a pole line or similar overhead structures; it may be self-supporting or installed on a supporting messenger cable.

aerial conductor. A conductor erected overhead.

aerodynamics. The science which deals with the motion of air and its mechanical effect when in motion.

afterglow. A fluorescent glow visible in an exhausted container of glass after removal from electrostatic influence.

agone. A line on the earth's surface on which the magnetic needle points to the true north, the magnetic meridian coinciding with the geographical.

aggregate. Inert material mixed with cement and water to produce concrete.

air-blast transformer. A transformer cooled by forced circulation of air through the core and coils of the transformer.

air circuit breaker. A circuit breaker in which the interruption occurs in air.

air changes. A method of expressing the amount of air leakage into or out of a building or room in terms of the number of building volumes or room volumes exchanged per unit of time.

air circulation. Natural or imparted motion of air.

2

air conditioner, room. A factory made assembly designed as a unit for mounting in a window, through a wall, or as a console. It is designed for free delivery of conditioned air without ducts.

air duct. Any passage to guide ventilating air.

air gap. A path for electrical energy through air, between two electrodes or core sections of a transformer.

air insulation. Insulation procured by the action of air.

alarm signal. A signal for attracting attention to some abnormal condition.

alarm system. An assembly of equipment and devices arranged to signal the presence of a hazard requiring urgent attention.

alive. Electrically connected to a source of potential difference, or electrically charged so as to have a potential different from that of ground.

alkaline battery. A storage battery in which the electrolyte consists of an alkaline solution, usually potassium hydroxide.

alloy. A mixture of two or more metals, as of copper and zinc to form brass.

alternating currents. The term alternating current refers to a current that reverses at regular recurring intervals of time and that has alternately positive and negative values.

alternating current (advantages). As compared with DC, the advantage of AC is the reduced cost of transmission by use of high voltage transformers.

3

alternating currents (disadvantages). As compared with DC, the disadvantages of AC are: The high voltage which renders it dangerous and requires more efficient insulation; alternating current cannot be used for such purposes as electroplating, charging storage batteries, etc.

alternating current (effects). There are several effects of the AC to consider in determining the size of wires. Accordingly, allowance must be made for: Self-induction, mutual induction, power factor, skin effect, eddy currents, frequency, resistance, electric hysteresis, etc.

alternating cycle. In an alternating current, a series of current changes which are regularly repeated. The cycle begins with zero current which rises to a positive maximum, falls to zero again, then to a negative maximum and returns to zero; the completion cycle is called a period and the number of periods accomplished in a second is the frequency of alternations. The maximum value of voltage or current attained is the amplitude.

alternation. A change of direction. A change of direction by an electromotive current. An AC cycle has two alternations, one positive and one negative alternation.

alternator. A machine for furnishing an alternating current.

aluminum wire. An electric conductor composed of commercially 99% pure aluminum. As compared with copper, aluminum wire has 62% conductivity.

amber. Often called "an organic jewel" is a harden tree resin that is millions of years old. The Greek word for amber is elektron. Rubbed amber would attract light objects.

ambient temperature. The temperature of air or other medium surrounding an electrical device.

4

American "Twist Joint". A simple method of connecting the ends of two sections of wire by tightly twisting the ends around each other for a few turns.

American Wire Gauge. A.W.G. or B & S (Brown & Sharpe) is a measurement of wire sizes.

ammeter. Measures the current flow in amperes in a circuit. An ammeter is connected in series in the circuit.

amortisseur. An arrangement of copper rods in the pole faces of a dynamo so as to dampen the oscillations of the magnetic flux at the commutator, and thus reduce the tendency of sparking at the brushes.

amortisseur winding. A "winding" similar to the squirrel cage winding of an induction motor, embedded in the field pole pieces of an alternator or synchronous condenser, to prevent hunting. In operation the heavy currents induced in the amortisseur winding when the machines get out of step tend to quickly re-establish the phase relation.

ampacity. The current in amperes a conductor can carry **continuously** under the conditions of use without exceeding its temperature rating.

ampere. The practical unit of electric current flow. If a one ohm resistance is connected to a one volt source, one ampere will flow.

ampere-hour. A current of one ampere flowing for one hour. The quantity of electricity passed by one ampere in one hour; being equal to 3,600 coulombs.

ampere meter. An instrument which measures the current strength directly in amperes. Also called an **ammeter.**

ampere-turn. A unit of magnetizing force equal to the number of amperes of current multiplied by the number of turns in the winding in which it flows.

5

amplidyne. A rotary magnetic or dynamo-electric amplifier used in servomechanism and control applications.

amplification. The process of increasing the strength (current, power, or voltage) of a signal.

amplifier. A device used to increase the signal voltage, current, or power, generally composed of a vacuum tube and associated circuit called a stage. It may contain several stages in order to obtain a desired gain.

amplitude. The maximum instantaneous value of the current strength or voltage attained during the cycle of an alternating current.

anemometer. An instrument for measuring the velocity of air in motion.

angle of lead. The forward angular departure from the established position, which the collecting brushes must be required to undergo on a commutator of a generator, to the end, that quiet commutation may be obtained.

anode. The positive pole of a battery, or preferably the path by which the current passes out and enters the electrolyte on its way to the other pole; opposed to the cathode.

annunciator. An electrically controlled signal board or indicator.

apparent power. In a reactive alternating current circuit, the product of volts and amperes which are not in phase, measured by volt-amperes. The product of root-mean-square current and the root-mean-square voltage.

appliance. A utilization item of electric equipment, usually complete in itself, generally other than industrial, normally built in standardized sizes or types that transforms electric energy into another form, usually heat or mechanical motion, at the point of utilization.

6

appliance branch circuit. A circuit supplying energy to one or more outlets to which appliances are to be connected; such circuits to have no permanently connected lighting fixtures not a part of an appliance.

appliance, cord and plug connected. A unit to be connected to the power source by means of a supply cord, and moved for reasons of interchange or realignment of the units.

appliance, fixed. An appliance which is fastened or otherwise secured at a specific location.

appliance, portable. An appliance which is actually moved or can easily be moved from one place to another in normal use.

appliance, stationary. A cord-connected appliance that is intended to be fastened in place or located in a dedicated space.

approved. Acceptable to the authority having jurisdiction.

aqueous solution. Substances dissolved in water.

arc. Unwanted flow of electricity through an insulating medium. A flash caused by an electric current ionizing a gas or vapor.

area, critical care. An area where patients ordinarily are intentionally exposed to electrical devices such as an intensive care area, an operating room, or an anesthetizing location.

area, inaccessible. An area in which people cannot freely move about, such as a crawl space.

armature. In a dynamo or alternator, that part of the machine in which currents are induced. In an induction motor it is the squirrel cage; the movable portion of a magnetic circuit. The moving part of a relay or vibrator.

7

armored cable. Two or more individually insulated conductors, wrapped in an insulating cover and enclosed within an interlocking, spirally-wound, galvanized steel cover.

arrester. A device intended to limit voltage by use of two or more electrodes in an enclosed medium or a solid-state conductor.

artificial ground. A grounding electrode, metal plate or pipe, buried in the earth.

askarel. A generic term for a group of nonflammable, synthetic chlorinated hydrocarbons used as electrical insulating media.

astatic. Having no magnetic power of direction.

asynchronous. Happening or acting without simultaneity.

asynchronous AC motor. A motor, the speed of which is not simultaneous with that of its driving generator; the two machines having an equal number of poles.

atom. The smallest particle of matter that can exist and still retain its identity as an element. An atom is formed of positive and negative particles of electricity, that is, of protons and electrons.

attachment plug (plug cap) (cap). A device which, by insertion in a receptacle, establishes connection between the conductors of the attached flexible cord and the conductors connected permanently to the receptacle.

attenuator. An adjustable transducer for reducing the amplitude of a wave without introducing appreciable distortion. A network of resistors used to reduce voltage, current, or power delivered to a load.

automatic. Self-acting, operating by its own mechanism when actuated by some impersonal influence; as for example, a change in current strength, pressure, temperature, or mechanical configuration.

8

automatically controlled. A system for which (1) energization of a motor, a magnet, a solenoid, or the like will occur without manual intervention, or (2) during any single predetermined cycle of operation, automatic changing of the mechanical load can reduce the speed of a motor sufficiently to re-establish starting-winding connections to the branch circuit.

automatic starter. One designed to automatically control the acceleration of a motor.

autotransformer. A type of transformer in which one winding serves for both primary and secondary. Autotransformers are used where the ratio of transformation is small, as a considerable savings in copper and iron can be affected, and the whole transformer reduced in size as compared with one having separate windings.

autotransformer starter. One having an autotransformer to furnish a reduced voltage for starting. The device includes the necessary switching mechanism and is frequently called a compensator or autostarter.

auxiliary relay. A relay whose function is to assist another relay or control device in performing a general function by supplying supplementary actions.

average efficiency of motor. The efficiency of a motor founded on its mean load. The ratio of a motor's performance in a specified time to the electric power it has consumed in the same time.

average volts and amperes. Since the sine curve is used to represent the alternating current, the average value may be defined as: The average of all the ordinates of the curve for one half of a cycle. The average value is used in some calculations, but, like the maximum value, not very often. The relation between the average and virtual value is of importance as it gives the form factor. Calling maximum value 1, average value = .637.

9

B

B.S.G. An abbreviation of British standard gauge.

B.W.G. An abbreviation of Birmingham wire gauge.

back pitch. The pitch backward of the windings of an armature.

backfill. Loose earth placed outside foundation walls for filling and grading.

back-pitch of armature. Turns of an armature current which have a tendency to demagnetize the field. Back ampere turns.

bad earth. A name given to a bad ground, or an earth connection with a comparatively strong electric resistance.

baffle. An object placed in an appliance to direct or to retard the flow of air or flue gases.

bakelite. Trade name for material compound chiefly of a phenol compound. It is manufactured in many forms and is a good insulating compound.

balanced circuit. A circuit, in which two branches are electrically alike and symmetrical with respect to a common reference point, usually ground.

balanced polyphase system. A polyphase system of electric distribution having current and phase symmetrically distributed through all its branches.

balanced three-wire system. A three-wire system in which no current flows in the conductor connected to the neutral point of the supply.

ballast. Devices that by means of inductance, capacitance, or resistance, singly or in combination, limit the lamp current of fluorescent or mercury lamps, to the required value for proper operation, and also, where necessary, provide the required starting voltage and current.

ballast noise rating. Ballast noise ratings are designated by letters starting with letter A - the quietest - up through F. The rating A is best for applications where the surrounding and competitive noise level may be at a minimum.

bamboo filament. An early form of incandescent lamp filament devised by Edison. It consists of fiber derived from bamboo and subjected to the carbonizing process.

banana plug. A single-conductor plug with a spring metal tip that somewhat resembles a banana in shape.

banjo. In pole line construction, a contrivance for tightening a wire, consisting of a drum mounted upon a kite-shaped board.

bank. An aggregation of similar devices connected together and used in cooperation.

bank of transformers. A number of transformers grouped together for convenience in changing the voltage.

bar armature. An armature the conductors of which are constructed of bars.

bar hanger. In house wiring, a device for supporting outlet boxes.

bar windings. Armature windings constructed of copper bars.

barb bolt. In machinery, one having jagged edges to prevent retraction after driving. Sometimes referred to as a rag bolt.

bare conductor. A conductor having no covering or electrical insulation whatsoever.

barette. A short bar in which the lights are closely spaced so that from a distance they appear to be a linear light. Barettes are usually less than 15 feet in length.

barometer. An instrument for measuring the pressure of the atmosphere.

barrel plating. Mechanical plating in which the cathodes are kept loosely in a container that rotates.

barrier. An insulating block placed between switch contacts of opposite polarity so that they may be placed close together without danger of a flashover.

barring hole. A hole in the rotor to permit insertion of a pry bar for the purpose of turning the rotor.

battery. A device that transforms chemical energy into electric energy. Two or more primary or secondary cells connected together electrically. The term does not apply to a single cell.

battery electrolyte. Solid, liquid, or aqueous alkali or acidic solution that permits ionic conduction between positive and negative electrodes of a cell.

battery solution. The fluid or electrolyte of the primary or secondary cell.

beacon. A light used to indicate a geographic location.

bearing wall. Wall supporting a load other than its own weight.

bell. An electromagnetical noisemaking device using a hammer to hit a gong; used in alarm systems.

belted-type cable. A multiple conductor cable having a layer of insulation over the assembled insulated conductors.

benchboard. A combination of a control desk and a vertical or enclosed switchboard in a common assembly.

bench mark. Point of reference from which measurements are made.

betty. A round iron bar flattened to a chisel like expansion at one end and used generally for the application of a large leverage for a temporary purpose.

bight of cable. One loop or bend only of cable.

bimetallic element. Two pieces of metal welded together so that they function as one piece. They are used in thermostats, thermometers, and other heat sensing devices. A bimetal will bend in one direction when heated and return to the original position when cooled to the original temperature.

bimetallic wire. A steel wire with an external coating of copper. It can be used for long spans because of the high tensile strength of the steel; composite wire.

binding post. A metal post furnished with a screw for securing the end of wires on electrical apparatus.

biphase. A term sometimes used for two phase.

bipolar. Having two magnetic poles, north and south; two-pole.

bisect. To divide into two equal parts.

bitumen. Tar, pitch, or asphalt.

blade. The movable contact member of a switch.

bleeder. A resistor connected across a power source to improve voltage regulation.

block. A square or portion of a city, town, or village which is enclosed by streets and including the alleys so enclosed; but not any street.

blocking relay. An auxiliary relay whose function is to render another relay or device ineffective under specified conditions.

blowing a fuse. The melting or fusing of a safety fuse resulting from the passage of the current through it exceeding the carrying capacity of the heat strip.

blowing point of a fuse. That degree of current strength which melts or blows the fuse.

blowout coil. An electromagnetic device that establishes a magnetic field in the space where an electric circuit is broken and helps to extinguish the arc.

bolometer. An instrument of great sensitivity; may be used to measure nonelectrical quantities, such as gas pressure or concentration, as well as current and radiant power.

bonding. The permanent joining of metallic parts to form an electrically conductive path which will assure electrical continuity and the capacity to conduct safely any current likely to be imposed.

bonding electric cables. The electric interconnecting of cable sheaths or armor to sheaths or armor of adjacent conductors.

bonding jumper. A reliable conductor to assure the required electrical conductivity between metal parts required to be electrically connected.

bonding jumper, circuit. The connection between portions of a conductor in a circuit to maintain required ampacity of the circuit.

bonding jumper, equipment. The connection between two or more portions of the equipment grounding conductor.

bonding jumper, main. The connection between the grounded circuit conductor and the equipment grounding conductor at the service.

booster. A transformer or generator inserted in a circuit to increase the voltage to overcome line drop.

bootleg. A protection for track wires when the wires leave the conduit or ground near the rail.

borderlight. A striplight placed behind a stage border on rigging.

bound charge. An electric charge which remains in an insulated conductor due to a nearby charge of opposite polarity.

bracket. A type hanger that is attached only at one end directly to a vertical surface of the building structure.

braided cable. A cable in which the wires are interlaced or braided instead of twisted.

braided wire. An electric conductor protected by an interwoven insulating covering.

braking. In electric braking, using the motors as dynamos, driving them by the energy due to the momentum of the cars.

braking resistor. A resistor commonly used in some type of dynamic braking systems, the prime purpose of which is to convert the electric energy developed during dynamic braking into heat and to dissipate this energy to the atmosphere.

branch circuit. The circuit conductors between the final overcurrent device protecting the circuit and the outlet(s).

branch circuit, appliance. A branch circuit supplying energy to one or more outlets to which appliances are to be connected; such circuits to have no permanently connected lighting fixtures not a part of an appliance.

branch circuit, individual. A branch circuit that supplies only one utilization equipment.

branch circuit, multiwire. A branch circuit consisting of two or more ungrounded conductors having a potential difference between them, and a grounded conductor having equal potential difference between it and each ungrounded conductor of the circuit and which is connected to the neutral conductor of the system.

brass. A yellow alloy composed of copper and zinc in various proportions. In some grades tin or lead is added in small amounts.

brazing. The art or process of joining metals together (brass alloy).

bread and butter cable. A term describing a variety of submarine cable lightly sheathed with alternate layers of wire and yarn.

break. The break of a circuit-opening device is the minimum distance between the stationary and movable contacts when the device is in its open position.

breakdown voltage. The voltage at which the insulation between two conductors will break down.

breaker points. Metal contacts that open and close a circuit at timed intervals.

breather. A device fitted in the wall of an explosionproof compartment, or connected by piping thereto, that permits relatively free passage of air through it, but that will not permit the passage of incendiary sparks or flames in the event of gas ignition inside the compartment.

bridge circuit. Two parallel paths connected between a common source of potential, with each path divided into two at intermediate junction points, and with an indicating element (galvanometer) bridged from one of the junctions to the other.

bridging. System of bracing between floor beams to distribute floor load.

bridle wire. Insulated wire for connecting conductors of an open wire line to associated pole-mounted apparatus.

brine. A salt solution.

Britannia joint. A method of connecting lengths of telephone or telegraph wires, in which the two ends, after being carefully scraped, are laid side by side for a distance of about two inches, an inch or so at the end of each being previously turned up at right angles, then wound tightly with several turns of binding wire, and the whole carefully soldered.

British thermal unit (B.t.u.). The quantity of heat required to raise the temperature of one pound of water by one degree F.

bronze. A varying alloy of copper and tin, with occasionally zinc or lead added. The copper varies from 80% to 90% and the tin from 10% to 20%. The greater portion of the tin makes a harder metal but decreases the tensile strength.

bronze conductor. A conductor made wholly of an alloy of copper with other than pure zinc. The copper may be alloyed with tin, cadmium, silicon, manganese, or phosphorus, or several of these in combination.

brush. A conductor, usually composed in part of some form of the element carbon, for drawing from the commutator the electric current generated by the armature of a dynamo.

B & S Gauge. The standard gauge used in the United States to specify wire sizes (Brown & Sharpe).

buck arm. A crossarm placed approximately at right angles to the line crossarm and used for supporting branch or lateral conductors.

buffer. An isolating circuit used to avoid reaction of a driven circuit upon the corresponding driving circuit.

bucking coil. A coil so connected as to oppose other coils.

building. A structure which stands alone or which is cut off from adjoining structures by fire walls with all openings therein protected by approved fire doors.

bulb. The glass globe in which the filament of an incandescent electric lamp is used.

bullet switch. A special type of momentary switch that can be operated either by pushing directly on the plunger or by sliding an object past it; can be used for a concealed installation on double-hung windows.

bull ring. A metal ring used in overhead construction at the junction point of three or more guy wires.

bull switch. An externally-operated wall-mounted safety switch which may or may not contain overcurrent protection, that is designed for the connection of portable cables and cords.

bunched cable. A cable enclosing two or more conductors.

buried cable. A cable laid directly in the ground without being enclosed is a conduit.

burnish. To rub a material to smooth or polish it.

burnisher. A tiny, ultra-fine file used to clean relay contacts.

burn out. The damaging of any portion of an electric machine by the accidental passage through it of a high voltage current.

bus. A conductor, or group of conductors, that serve as a common connection for two or more circuits.

bus bars. Heavy copper bars connected with all the dynamos in a central station in order to receive the entire electrical output, and carry the distributing conductors of the system.

bushing. A fitting provided to protect wires from abrasion, and intended for use where conductors enter or leave a raceway system. A conduit bushing is an internally threaded fitting intended for use on rigid conduit.

busway. A protective enclosure for buses (conductors formed by large cross section bars or rods).

butt joint. A method joining lengths of wire by setting them end to end and welding or soldering them together.

buzzer. An electric call signal which makes a buzzing noise caused by the rapid vibrations of an armature.

buzz stick. A device for testing suspension insulator units for fault when the units are in position on an energized line.

BX. Trade name for a type AC armored cable.

C

"C" clamp. A hanger that grips a flange by means of a jaw and setscrew combination.

cabinet. An enclosure designed either for surface or flush mounting and provided with a frame, mat, or trim in which a swinging door or doors are or may be hung.

cable. Either a stranded conductor (single conductor cable) or a combination of conductors insulated from one another (multiple-conductor cable). The component conductors of the second kind of cable may either be solid or stranded and this kind of cable may or may not have a common insulating covering. The first kind of cable is a single conductor, while the second kind is a group of several conductors. The term "cable" is applied by some manufacturers to a solid wire heavily insulated and lead-covered; this usage arises from the manner of the insulation, but such a conductor is not included under this definition of "cable." The term "cable" is a general one, and in practice, it is usually applied only to the larger sizes. A small cable is called "a stranded wire" or a "cord." Cables may be bare or insulated, and the latter may be armored with lead, or with steel wires or bands.

cable casing. The outside coating or sheath of a cable.

cable cell. A primary cell produced in a defective cable by a broken strand of the conducting core and the metallic sheath acting together as electrodes.

cable entrance fitting. A fitting used to seal or attach the cable sheath or armor to the pothead.

cable grip. A clamp secured to the end of an underground cable so that it may be readily drawn through a conduit.

cable jacks. In line construction, a pair of supports for raising the axle of a cable reel so that the drum may freely rotate in paying out the cable.

cable joint. Also termed a "splice"; a connection between two or more individual lengths of cables, with their conductors individually connected, and with protecting sheaths over the joint.

cable service. Service conductors arranged in the form of a cable.

cable sheath. A lead alloy protective covering on cables of various types.

cable spinning jenny. A contrivance for adjusting an overhead cable to the messenger wire; a cable winder.

cable terminal pole. In overhead cable construction, the last pole on a line carrying the cable head.

cable worming. Hemp or similar material, forming a core about which to wind the conductors of a cable.

cadmium. A white metal with bluish tinge belonging to the same chemical family as zinc, which it closely resembles.

cadmium test. A storage battery test made with a rod of cadmium.

cadmium test voltmeter. A voltmeter used for testing the voltage of storage batteries on charge or discharge.

cage lightning protector. A wire lightning arrester built like a cage around the protected object.

calcium light. A very intense white light produced by the incandescence of a ball of lime in the flame of combined oxygen and hydrogen gases; limelight.

calculus. A method of calculating which consists in the investigation of the infinitesimal changes of quantities when the relations between the quantities are known.

calibrate. To ascertain by special measurement, or by comparison with a standard, variations in the readings of a galvanometer or other instrument for electrical measurement.

calibration. The process of dividing and numbering the scale of an instrument; also of correcting and determining the error of an existing scale.

calorescence. The conversion of invisible rays of heat into light rays by converging them to a focus upon a suitable substance which may thereby be heated to incandescence.

calorie. The French heat unit.

calorific. In physics, a term meaning heating; heat producing.

calorimeter. An instrument used for measuring the heat generated by an electrical current in a conductor.

calorimetric test. A test in which the losses in a machine are deduced from the heat produced by them. The losses are calculated from the temperature rises produced by this heat in the coolant or in the surrounding media.

cam. A revolving disc, usually of a spiral eccentric, or heart shape, fixed on a shaft or such other form as to impart to a lever, rod, or block in contact with it, such variable velocity or motion as may be required.

cancellation. The process of shortening calculations by rejecting equal factors from numerator and denominator, that is, from dividend and divisor.

candelabra lampholder. A lampholder having a nominal screw diameter of 1/2 inch.

candle. A unit of illumination; being the light given by a British standard candle at the distance of one foot.

candle lumen. A term sometimes employed for the lumen.

candlepower. A unit of light equal to the intensity from a standard candle.

canned. Completely enclosed and sealed by a metal sheath.

canopy. A metal cover set at the point where an electric light fixture or pendant enters a wall or ceiling, to conceal the connections.

caoutchouc. A vegetable substance obtained from the juice of certain tropical trees, valued for its superior rubber insulating properties.

capacitance. Measure, in farads, or the opposition to voltage changes in an AC circuit, causing voltage to lag behind current; exhibited by condensers, two conductors separated by a nonconductor.

capacitive circuit. One containing more capacitive reactance than inductive reactance.

capacitive reactance. The effect of capacitance in opposing the flow of alternating or pulsating current.

capacitor. A device used to boost the voltage to a motor. Running capacitors are used in the starting winding to increase the running torque of the motor. Starting capacitors are used in the starting winding to increase the starting torque of the motor. Two electrodes or sets of electrodes in the form of plates, separated from each other by an insulating material called the dielectric.

capacitor motor. A split-phase motor in which a condenser displaces part of the current in phase from the remainder in order that the motor may be self-starting on single phase supply current.

capacity. The property of a system of conductors and dielectrics which permits the storage of electric charges.

capacity effect. In an AC circuit, an effect exactly opposite to that of inductance; that is, it assists the current to rise to its maximum value sooner than it would otherwise.

capacity of conductor. The quantity of electricity with which either plate must be charged in order to raise its electrical pressure from zero to unity.

capacity of storage battery. The amount of energy which a storage cell is capable of accumulating; it is generally calculated in ampere hours; that is, the product of the number of amperes which the cell can discharge into the number of hours through which it can maintain that discharge.

capillarity. The peculiar action of a liquid by which its surface at the line of contact with a solid is raised or lowered.

cap screw. A screw bolt intended to be used without a nut.

carbon. One of the nonmetallic elements; it exists almost pure in three forms, of which two are crystalline; (1) diamond, (2) graphite, and (3) noncrystalline, charcoal.

carbon brushes. Commutator brushes made of strips of prepared carbon, sometimes coated with copper to increase conductivity.

carborundum. A silicide of carbon used as an abrasive; harder than emery.

carcel. The French unit of illumination, equal to 9 1/2 British candles.

cardan joint. The universal joint used in machinery to permit flexibility of motion in a shaft.

carrying capacity. The maximum current strength that a conductor can safely transmit.

Carter system. The so-called "Carter" system of multi-location lighting control is one where two or more 3-way or 4-way switches are connected to both sides of the line. By using a 3-conductor the lights could be controlled with two 3-way switches and also have a hot receptacle. This was permitted in 1920, but not today.

cartridge fuse. A fuse enclosed with an insulating and protective covering and provided with connections at its ends.

cast iron conduit. For underground conduits, cast iron pipe is used similar to ordinary wrought iron pipe, except that it is thicker.

cataphoresis. The tendency to mix or become equably diffused as referred to electricity. Electric osmosis.

cataphoretic electrode. An electrode which holds in solution the chemical which is to enter into the body by cataphoresis. The anode.

catenary system. This system derives its name from the curve formed by a flexible cable suspended between two supports and in its simple form consists of a steel messenger cable supported on insulators and thus forming a catenary curve.

cathode. The electrode through which a direct current leaves a liquid, gas, or other discrete part of an electrical circuit.

cat's whisker. The fine wire used in some type of crystal detectors to make contact with the crystal.

caustic soda. Sodium hydrate. An alkali prepared by the reaction between sodium carbonate and lime. It is employed as the electrolyte in the Edison primary cell.

cavity. That portion of the microwave cooking appliance in which food may be heated, cooked, or dried.

cavity wall. Wall built of solid masonry units arranged to provide air space within the wall.

ceiling rose, or rosette. An ornamental ceiling block in the form of a rose for suspending an incandescent lamp.

ceiling, suspended. A part of a building structure that is located on the room side of the structural ceiling and that generally provides a plenum area above it for wiring that may or may not be accessible by service personnel.

cell (battery). A single element of an electric battery, either primary or secondary, usually the former.

cell (as applied to raceways). A single, enclosed tubular space in a cellular metal floor member, the axis of the cell being parallel to the axis of the metal floor member.

cellular metal floor raceway. A raceway formed in the hollow spaces of cellular metal floors, together with its fittings.

celluloid filament. An incandescent lamp filament composed of a celluloid thread reduced to carbon.

cellulosic. A paper or wood type product that is treated or processed. For example; insulation, paper, fiber, and the like.

celluvert fiber. A preparation used for insulating purposes.

Celsius thermometer. The centigrade thermometer, so called from its inventor Andre Celsius. The freezing point is zero degrees and the boiling point 100 degrees.

cement arch conduit. A form of conduit for underground wires consisting of arched ducts composed of equal parts of Portland cement & sand molded around wire gauze.

cement copper. Copper extracted from water pumped out of copper mines.

centenary curve. The curve or sag formed by the weight of a wire hanging freely between two points of suspension.

center of distribution. In any distribution system, that point from which electrical energy must be supplied to use a minimum weight of conducting material.

Centigrade. The European scale of measuring temperature. 0 represents temperature of freezing ice, 100 the temperature of boiling water at sea level.

centimeter. Unit of metric system of measurement, equals approximately .39 inch; 1/100th of a meter.

centrifugal clutch. An automatic device sometimes used with split phase motors which, below a predetermined speed, permits the rotating element of a motor to revolve free of the shaft, and which at that predetermined speed engages the shaft to make it turn with the rotating element and transmit the motor's power through it.

centrifugal starting-switch. A centrifugally operated automatic mechanism used to perform a circuit-changing function in the primary winding of a single-phase induction motor after the rotor has attained a predetermined speed, and to perform the reverse circuit-changing operation prior to the time the rotor comes to rest.

chain lightning. A flash of lightning which appears in a long zig-zag or broken line.

chain or nested winding. A three-phase, two range winding. The adjacent coils link one another as in a chain, the center of one set of coils being occupied by the sides of coils of the other phases.

27

chamber of incandescent lamp. The glass vacuum bulb containing the carbon filament.

chandelier. A frame with branches to hold candle sockets; also an ornamental arrangement of pipes and fixtures to hold devices for lighting.

charge. In storage battery work, the amount of current absorbed by the battery during the operation of "charging." A storage battery charge is measured in ampere hours.

charging a storage battery. The operation of sending a flow of current through a storage battery to bring the plates into condition to cause a flow of current on discharge. The charging current should be in proportion to the ampere hour capacity of the cell. Charging voltage should be at least 10% higher than the normal voltage of the battery when charged.

chase. Recess in inner face of masonry wall providing space for pipes and/or ducts.

chemical effect of the current. If the conductor is a liquid which is a chemical compound of a certain class called electrolyte, the liquid will be decomposed at the place where the current enters and leaves it.

chemical generator. A name given to a primary battery, as distinguished from a dynamo or mechanical generator.

chime. An electromechanical noisemaking device that uses a plunger to strike one or two tone bars. Commonly used as a doorbell.

chimney effect. The tendency of air or gas in a duct or other vertical passage to rise when heated due to its lower density compared with that of the surrounding air or gas.

chlorate. A salt of chloric acid. All chlorates are soluble in water; on heating they evolve much oxygen and a trace of chlorine, the residue being a chloride.

chloride cell. A type of cell having elaborately prepared negative plates in which lead grids are cast around small hexagonal slabs or "pastilles" of chloride of lead.

choke coil. A coil of wire with iron or air core wound in such a manner as to acquire self-induction to a high degree when employed on alternating current circuits. A reactance coil that has low ohmic resistance and high impedance to alternating current.

chronometer. An instrument operated by electricity for measuring time and adjusting for accuracy under changing conditions.

circle diagram. A graphic method by means of which many of the properties of induction motors and several other types of AC motors can be graphically investigated.

circuit. A complete path over which an electric current can flow.

circuit breaker. A device designed to open and close a circuit by nonautomatic means and to open the circuit automatically on a predetermined overcurrent without injury to itself when properly applied within its rating. Circuit breakers can be reset.

circuit, multiple or parallel. A multiple or parallel circuit consists of two or more circuits connected to the common junction points so that the same potential drop is established through each branch.

circuit, series. A circuit supplying energy to a number of devices connected in series. The same current passes through each device in completing its path to the source of supply.

circuit, single-phase. A single-phase circuit is either an alternating current circuit which has only two points of entry or one which, having more than two points of entry, is intended to be so energized that the potential differences between all pairs of points of entry are either in phase or differ in phase by 180 degrees.

circuit, three-phase. A three-phase circuit is a combination of circuits energized by alternating electromotive forces which differ in phase by one-third of a cycle, 120 degrees.

circuit-to-ground voltage. The rated value of voltage with respect to earth ground.

circuit voltage. The greatest effective difference of potential between any two conductors in a given circuit.

circular inch. The area of a circle whose diameter is one inch; as distinguished from one square inch and equals .7854 square inch. The circular inches in any circle is simply the diameter in inches squared.

circular mil. The area of a circle one mil (.001") in diameter (cma). The area of a wire in circular mils is equal to the square of the diameter in mils. Thus a wire 2 mils in diameter (.002") has a cross sectional area of $2 \times 2 = 4$ circular mils. Accordingly, to obtain the area of a wire in circular mils, measure its diameter with a micrometer which reads directly in mils or thousandths of an inch, and square the reading.

circular mil foot. A unit of conductor size, equal to a portion of the conductor having a cross-sectional area of one circular mil and length of one foot.

circumference. The curved line that bounds a circle.

clamp, outlet box. Part of a box intended to secure raceway, tubing, or cable to the box.

clamp terminals. Terminals in the form of screw clamps for uniting the ends of wires.

clapper. An armature that is hinged or pivoted.

Class II. Low voltage, limited energy electrical systems. Most alarm systems meet Class II requirements.

clearing time. The time elapsing from the beginning of an overcurrent condition to the final circuit interruption. The clearing time is equal to the sum of the melting time and the arcing time.

cleat, electric. A small block of suitable grooved wood, or other insulating material for securing electric wires to the walls or ceiling of a room.

cleat wiring. A method of supporting wiring on porcelain insulators or cleats. By the use of cleats, both wires of a circuit are held at the correct distance apart by each cleat.

cleavage electricity. Electricity resulting from the splitting of mica or other crystalline minerals.

clerestory. That part of a building that rises clear of the roofs or other parts and whose walls contain windows for lighting the interior.

clevis hanger. A type of split ring hanger.

climbers. Spurs strapped to a lineman's boots to assist him in climbing a pole; also called climbing irons.

climbing space. The vertical space reserved along the side of a pole or tower to permit ready access for linemen to equipment and conductors.

clip, fuse. Contacts on a fuse support for connecting a fuse holder into a circuit.

clockwise. Said of rotating parts of machinery, when they run right-handed or as the hands of a clock, from left to right.

closed circuit. A circuit permitting a continuous current.

closed-circuit transition. As applied to reduced-voltage controllers, including star-delta controllers, a method of starting in which the power to the motor is not interrupted during the starting sequence.

closed loop. A signal path that includes a forward path, a feedback path, and a summing point and that forms a closed circuit.

closed-loop series street lighting. Street lighting system that employs two-wire series circuits in which the return wire is always adjacent.

closing coil. A coil used in electromagnets that supplies power for closing the device.

closing relay. A form of auxiliary relay used to control the closing and opening of the closing circuit of the device so that the main closing current does not pass through the control switch or other initiating device.

clown's hat curve. A voltage or current curve which undergoes rapid changes in value, suggesting in shape the pointed hat worn by clowns.

clubfoot electromagnet. A horseshoe electromagnet having a magnetizing coil wound upon only one of its poles.

coarse winding. The few turns of thick insulated wire joined in series with the armature, employed in winding the field magnet of a series wound or compound wound dynamo.

coating. In metallurgy, the process of covering metals with a superior metal as gilding, plating, silvering, galvanizing, etc.

coaxial cable. A transmission line consisting of two conductors concentric with and insulated from each other.

coaxial conductor. An electric conductor comprising outgoing and return current paths having a common axis, one of the paths completely surrounding the other throughout its length.

coded fire alarm system. A local fire alarm system in which the alarm signal is sounded in a predetermined coded sequence.

coefficient. In mathematics, a number or letter affixed to a quantity, to show how many times the quantity is to be taken. A coefficient is a multiplier or factor, and when it enters into a formula, represents some known value, usually found by experimenting.

coercive force. The magnetizing force necessary to remove all the magnetization remaining in a piece of magnetic material after the magnetizing force has been discontinued.

coercivity. The property of a magnetic material measured by the coercive force corresponding to the saturation induction for the material.

cogging. Variations in motor torque at very low speeds caused by variations in magnetic flux due to the alignment of the rotor and stator teeth at various positions of the rotor.

coherence. The act of cleaving or sticking together; cohesion.

coherer. Conducting particles constituting a semiconducting bridge between two electrodes and serving to detect electromagnetic waves.

cohesion. In physics, the principle or property by which the particles of a substance hold together, opposed to repulsion. In solids, cohesion is greater than repulsion, especially in the case of metals; with liquids, the two forces are about balanced, while in gases, the force of repulsion is far greater than that of attraction.

coil. An assemblage of successive convolutions of a conductor. A unit of a winding consisting of one or more insulated conductors connected in series and surrounded by common insulation, and arranged to link or produce magnetic flux.

coil and plunger. An electromagnet consisting of a hollow coil or spool having a free core which, upon the passage of an electric current through the coil, is drawn into it; a solenoid.

coincident. Occurring at the same time.

coked filament. An incandescent lamp filament of carbon which has been electrically heated in a vacuum to such a degree as to reduce it to coke.

cold drawn. A term applied in connection with wire or seamless tubes, which are drawn to size through rolls of dies while cold.

cold light. Luminous radiation unattended by obscure radiation. Fire-fly or glow-worm light.

collectors. Devices such as brushes and collecting rings, for drawing off current from the generating machine so that electricity may be utilized.

column. Verticle load-carrying member of a structural frame.

comb. A collector of electricity used on influence or frictional electric machines; it consists of a bar from which a number of teeth project like teeth of an ordinary comb.

combination fan and limit control. A control that cycles the fan and the main burner off and on in response to the temperature of a designated place in the heating equipment.

combination rubber tape. The assembly of both rubber and friction tape into one tape that provides both insulation and mechanical protection for joints.

combination system. An alarm system that employs both burglary and fire protection. The alarm system may also provide additional supervisory circuits, such as police call, medical alert, basement flooding, and the like.

comb lightning arrester. A multigap lightning arrester in which the gaps are formed by metal teeth opposite each other, resembling the teeth of a comb.

combustible material. Material made of or surfaced with wood, compressed paper, plant fibers, or other material that will ignite and burn, as applied to materials adjacent to or in contact with heat-producing appliances, chimney connectors and vent connectors, steam and hot water pipes, and warm air ducts. Such material shall be considered as combustible even though flameproofed, fire-retardant treated, or plastered.

come along. A wireman's tool used in drawing out wire to the proper tension. This tool is attached to a block and tackle, or drawn in by hand, and as soon as the proper force has been applied, the wire is held, while the lineman secures it to the insulator.

command. One of a set of several signals that occurs as a result of interpreting an instruction; the commands initiate the individual steps that form the process of executing the instruction's operation.

commercial equipment. Equipment intended to be used on commercial, industrial, or institutional premises, such as restaurants, schools, motels, public and commercial campsites, public swimming pools, beaches, and the like.

commissioning tests. Tests applied to rotating machinery at the site under normal service conditions to show that the machine has been erected and connected in a correct manner and is able to work satisfactorily.

common return. A single return conductor for several circuits.

communication. The transmission of information from one point to another by means of electromagnetic waves.

commutated currents. Said of the alternating currents induced in the armature of a dynamo when they have been converted into direct currents by the action of the commutator.

commutating-field winding. An assembly of field coils located on the commutating poles, that produces a field strength approximately proportional to the load current. This field winding is used alone, or supplemented by a compensating winding.

commutating pole (interpole). An auxiliary pole placed between the main poles of a commutating machine. Its exciting winding carries a current proportional to the load current and produces a flux in such a direction and phase as to assist the reversal of the current in the short-circuited coil.

commutation. Conversion of alternating current to direct current.

commutator. A ring of insulated copper segments connected to the windings of an armature, which bear brushes connecting the armature winding to the outside circuits to change the induced alternating current of the armature to direct current in the output.

commutator smoothing stone. A kind of stone used for grinding commutators. These stones consist of compounded abrasive material for grinding out scores or roughened and flat surfaces on commutators. A rubber stone is used as a final polish after grinding.

compactor, undercounter. An appliance intended for installation under a counter top and permanently attached to the building structure or to adjacent cabinets or appliances.

comparator. An instrument by means of which an AC ammeter or voltmeter may be calibrated with the DC standard. It is essentially a hot wire instrument which indicates zero when the AC and DC, to be compared, are equal.

compensated repulsion motor. A repulsion motor in which the primary winding on the stator is connected in series with the rotor winding via a second set of brushes on the commutator in order to improve the power factor and commutation.

compensator. A name sometimes given to the autotransformer which is a single coil transformer, in which the same winding will serve both as a primary and as a secondary. A type of stator for induction motors consisting of an autotransformer for each phase, with taps, thus providing variable inductances which are inserted in the field magnet circuit.

complement of angle. What is needed to make the value of an angle equal to a right angle or 90°.

complete fault. A defect which causes a complete break or interruption in an electric circuit.

complex fraction. One whose numerator or denominator is a fraction.

complex power. A term used in rotating machinery in which the active power is the real part and the reactive power, with sign reversed, is the imaginary part.

compliance. A property reciprocal to stiffness. Flexibility.

component. In mechanics, one of the parts of a stress or strain, out of which the whole may be compounded by the principle of the parallelogram of forces.

composite bushing. A bushing in which the insulation consists of several coaxial layers of different insulating materials.

composite cable. A multiconductor cable having conductors of more than one size.

composite conductor. A conductor consisting of two or more strands of different metals, operated in parallel.

composite wire. A compound bimetallic wire used in telegraph and telephone lines to secure both strength and conductivity; it consists of a core of iron or steel covered with a sheathing of copper; now superseded in best practice by hard drawn copper wire.

compound cable. A cable having a core made up of several wires stranded, or otherwise bound together.

compound motor. A DC motor in which the magnet coils have both series and shunt winds, therefore it is a combined series and shunt motor.

compound winding. In a common magnetic circuit, the winding connecting in series with the load.

compressor. The part of a mechanical refrigerating system which receives the refrigerant vapor at low pressure and compresses it into a smaller volume at higher pressure.

computer. A stored program, data-processing system. A machine for carrying out specified transformations on information.

concatenation. Linked together in series.

concealed. Rendered inaccessible by the structure or finish of the building. Wires in concealed raceways are considered concealed, even though they may become accessible by withdrawing them.

concealed knob and tube wiring. A method, running wires under floors and in partitions by supporting them on knobs and tubes. This method wiring should be discouraged as often as possible, as it is subject to mechanical injury and is liable to interference from rats, mice, etc. because the wires run according to this method are liable to sag against beams, laths, etc, or are likely to be covered by shavings or other inflammable building materials.

concentrated winding. An armature winding consisting of one coil, per phase, per pole.

concentration cell. An electrolyte cell, the electromotive force of which is due to differences in composition of the electrolyte at anode and cathode areas.

concentric. Having a common center.

concentric conductor. A tubular conductor containing an inner conducting core separated from it by insulation.

concrete-tight conduit fitting. A fitting so constructed that embedment in freshly mixed concrete will not result in the entrance of concrete into the fitting.

condensance. The reactance in an electric circuit due to capacity acting in the opposite direction to the reactance of the inductance.

condensate. Water formed by a change of state which occurs when the temperature of steam becomes less than that corresponding to its pressure.

condenser. An accumulator of electrical energy. A type largely used consists of layers of tin foil insulated from each other by sheets of parafined paper, oiled silk, mica, etc., sealed in an airtight case.

conducell. A cell like insulator used in a cable joint. Conducell for a three conductor cable consists of an outer seamless tube, three similarly formed curved inner separating pieces, and two end spacing rings. This assembly forms three separate cells for the conductor, the parts being interlocked among themselves.

conductance. The measure of ease with which a substance conducts electricity, measured in ohms. It is the opposite of resistance and is expressed in mhos.

conduction. The flow of an electric current through a conducting body, such as a metallic wire.

conductivity. The specific electric conductance of a substance, the relative power of carrying the electric current possessed by the different substances, the conducting power of pure copper being taken as the standard.

conductor. An electrical path which offers comparatively little resistance. A wire or combination of wires not insulated from one another, suitable for carrying a single electric current. Bus bars are also conductors. Conductors may be classed with respect to their conducting power as; (a) good; silver, copper, aluminum, zinc, brass, platinum, iron, nickle, tin, lead; (b) fair; charcoal and coke, carbon, plumbago, acid solutions, sea water, saline solutions, metallic ores, living vegetable substances, moist earth; (c) partial; water, the body, flame, linen, cotton, mahogany, pine, rosewood, lignum vitae, teak, and marble.

conductor, bare. A conductor having no covering or electrical insulation whatsoever.

conductor, covered. A conductor encased within material of composition or thickness that is not recognized by the Code as electrical insulation.

conductor, insulated. A conductor encased within material of composition and thickness that is recognized by the Code as electrical insulation.

conductor shielding. A conducting or semiconducting element in direct contact with the conductor and in intimate contact with the inner surface of the insulation so that the potential of this element is the same as the conductor.

conduit. An enclosure for conductors. For underground wiring there are numerous kinds of conduit; fiber, asbestos cement, metallic, soapstone, rigid polyvinyl chloride (PVC), fiberglass epoxy, etc.

conduit bender. A tool for bending pipe conduits; called a hickey.

conduit body. A separate portion of a conduit or tubing system that provides access through a removable cover(s) to the interior of the system, at a junction of two or more sections of the system, or at a terminal point of the system.

conduit fittings. Accessories used to complete a conduit system, such as boxes, bushings, and access fittings.

conduit, flexible metal. A flexible raceway of circular form for enclosing wires or cables; usually made of steel, wound helically and with interlocking edges, and with a weather resistant coating. Sometimes referred to as "Greenfield."

conduit hub. A female threaded connector that is integral with the box material for connection of threaded rigid conduit.

conduit, rigid steel. A raceway made of mild steel pipe with a weather-resistant coating.

conduit riser. A conduit upright.

conduit run. A duct bank; an arrangement of conduit with a continuous duct between two points in an electrical installation.

condulet. A conduit fitting.

conformity. The accuracy of its output; used especially in reference to a function potentiometer.

congelation. The process of passing, or the act of converting from a fluid to a solid state by the abstraction of heat. Freezing.

connected load. The sum of the continuous ratings of the load consuming apparatus, connected to the system or any part thereof.

connection. A finished electrical contact.

connector. A device to join conductors by soldering or mechanical means.

connector, pressure (solderless). A device that establishes a connection between two or more conductors or between one or more conductors and a terminal, by means of mechanical pressure, and without the use of solder.

console. A control cabinet located apart from the associated switching equipment, arranged to control those functions for which an operator or attendant is required.

constant current. Either a direct or alternating current which is maintained at a constant value, that is, unvarying amperage maintained automatically or otherwise.

contact. A terminal to which a connection can be made.

contact clip. The clip that the switchblade enters or embraces.

contact conductor. The part of the distribution system other than the track rails, that is in immediate electric contact with current collectors of the cars or locomotives.

contact gap. The final length of the isolating distance of a contact in the open position.

contactor. A device for repeatedly establishing and interrupting an electric power circuit.

contact rating. The capacity of electrical contacts to handle current and voltage.

contact resistance. Resistance resulting at the point of contact of several surfaces.

contacts. Metal pieces set at different points in an electrical circuit for conveniently making and breaking the circuit.

continuity of circuit. The state of a circuit which preserves an unbroken course throughout for the flow of electricity.

continuous duty. Operation at a substantially constant load for an indefinitely long time.

continuous load. A load where the maximum current is expected to continue for three hours or more.

continuous loading. A series loading in which the added inductance is uniformly distributed along the conductor.

contour line. On a land map denoting elevations, a line connecting points with the same elevation.

contracture. A state of rigidity of the muscles of the body sometimes resulting from the shock of an electric current.

control circuit (motor control). The circuit of a control apparatus or system that carries the electric signals directing the performance of the controller, but does not carry the main power current.

controller. A device or group of devices that serves to govern, in some predetermined manner, the electric power delivered to the apparatus to which it is connected.

control panel. An exposed or enclosed upright panel carrying switches and other protective, controlling, and measuring devices for electric machinery or equipment.

control relay. One used with an electrically operated device to control the closing or opening coil current of the device so that the main operating current does not pass through the control switch.

convection currents. The streams of charged particles flowing from the pointed end of a highly electrified insulated conductor; also called convection streams and electric wind.

convection of heat. (a) The effect produced by an electric current upon the temperature of an unevenly heated wire, (b) the transfer of heat by the motion of the heated matter itself; it can, therefore, take place only in liquids and gases.

converter. A revolving apparatus for converting alternating current into direct current or vice versa; it is usually called a rotary converter and is to be distinguished from the other methods such as by motor generator sets, mercury vapor rectifiers, electrolytic rectifiers, etc. A converter may be considered as any species of apparatus for changing electrical energy from one form into another.

conveyor. A mechanical contrivance, generally electrically driven, that extends from a receiving point to a discharge point and transports material between those points.

convolutions. The loops in a coil of wire.

cooking unit, counter-mounted. A cooking appliance designed for mounting in or on a counter and consisting of one or more heating elements, internal wiring, and built-in or separately mountable controls.

co-phasal alternations. Alternations having the same phases.

copper. A brownish-red metal, tough, malleable, and ductile. It can be cast, welded, forged, rolled, and drawn. Next to silver, it is the best conductor of electricity and heat known.

copper-clad aluminum conductors. Conductors drawn from a copper-clad aluminum rod with the copper metallurgically bonded to an aluminum core. The copper forms a minimum 10 percent of the cross-sectional area of a solid conductor or each strand of a stranded conductor.

copper-clad steel. Steel with a coating of copper welded to it, as distinguished from copper-plated or copper-sheathed material.

copper losses in transformers. Losses do to; heating of the conductors, eddy currents in conductors, stray losses, etc.

44

coppered plumbago. Plumbago in a powdered state, dusted with copper, used to prepare non-metallic surfaces for electroplating.

cord. A small cable, very flexible, and substantially insulated to withstand wear. There is no sharp dividing line in respect to size between a cord and a cable, and likewise no sharp dividing line in respect to the character of insulation between a cord and a stranded wire. Rubber is used as the insulating material for many classes of cords.

cord adjuster. A piece of equipment for altering the pendant length of a flexible cord of a pendant.

cord-connected unit. A unit intended for connection to the power source by means of a supply cord. Such a unit is intended to be moved for reasons of interchange or realignment of the units of a system.

cord connector body. A plug receptacle provided with means for attachment to flexible cords.

cord grip (strain relief). A piece of equipment by means of which the flexible cord entering a device or equipment is gripped in order to relieve the terminals from tension in the cord.

core. (a) The insulated electrical conductor of a cable, as distinguished from the outer covering or sheathing; (b) the mass of iron forming the interior portion of an electromagnet, and around which the coils are wound; (c) the metallic body of a dynamo or motor armature upon which the windings are built up; (d) the bundle of iron wires upon which the primary and secondary coils of an induction coil or transformer are wound.

core ducts. The space between or through core laminations provided to permit the radial or axial flow of ventilating air in rotating machinery.

core loss. The power dissipated in a magnetic core subjected to a time-varying magnetizing force. Core loss includes hysteresis and eddy current losses in the core.

core transformer. One having an iron core, upon which the wire is wound in such a manner that the iron is enveloped within the coils, the outer surface of the coils being exposed to the air.

core wire. A soft iron wire having practically no residual magnetism.

corkscrew rule. If the direction of travel of a right-handed corkscrew represents the direction of the current in a straight conductor, the direction of rotation of the corkscrew will represent the direction of the magnetic lines of force.

cornice lighting. Light sources shielded by a panel parallel to the wall and attached to the ceiling and distributing light over the wall.

corn plaster fuse. A cylindrical form of safety fuse provided in telephone switchboards.

corona effect. The particular form of the glow discharge that occurs in the neighborhood of electric conductors where the insulation is subject to electric stress.

correction. A quantity added to a calculated or observed value to obtain the true value.

corrective network. An electric network designed to be inserted in a circuit to improve its transmission properties, its impedance properties, or both.

corrosion. Chemical action which causes destruction of the surface of a metal, usually by oxidation or rusting, often by disintegrating influence of stray electric currents or ground return currents in electric systems, known as electrolytic corrosion; the metal may also be eaten away by the action of acids present in water or in the surrounding air. To diminish corrosion of exposed surfaces, paints, oils, or other protective coatings are employed.

corrosion-resistant material. A material having a resistance to corrosion equivalent to or exceeding that of a brass or bronze alloy.

cosine. In trigonometry, the sine of the complement of an angle. It may be represented as the length of the adjacent side or base of a triangle of which the sine is the perpendicular or opposite side, or as the ratio existing between the adjacent side or base and the hypotenuse.

cosine law. The intensity of illumination received obliquely is proportional to the cosine of the angle which the luminous rays make with the normal to the illuminated surface.

cotangent. In trigonometry, the tangent of the complement of an arc or angle.

cotter pin. A split key; properly a headless taper split pin, driven into its hole and expanded at the small end so that it cannot jar loose.

coulomb. A unit of electrical charge; the quantity of electricity passing in one second through a circuit in which the rate of flow is one ampere.

coulometer. An electrolytic cell arranged for the measurement of a quantity of electricity by the chemical action produced.

counterclockwise motion. A circular motion the reverse of the hands of a clock as seen when one reads the time.

counter electromotive force. An objectionable and unnecessarily long term for reverse pressure or reverse voltage.

counterpoise. A second aerial suspended on supports about one foot above the ground and insulated from the latter. The counterpoise should run parallel with and preferably underneath the main aerial, though if necessary, it may be offset to one side. Used in places where it is difficult to obtain a good ground.

couple. An element of a storage cell consisting of two plates, one positive and one negative.

coupling. A fitting intended to connect two lengths of raceway or perform a similar function.

couplings, pothead. Entrance fittings which may be provided with a rubber gland to provide a hermetic seal at the point where the cable enters the box.

cover. An unhinged, removable covering part.

covered conductor. A conductor encased within material of composition or thickness that is not recognized by the Code as electrical insulation.

cradle base. A piece of equipment that supports the machine at the bearing housings.

crawling. The stable but abnormal running of a synchronous or asynchronous machine at a speed near to a submultiple of the synchronous speed.

crawl space. Shallow space between the first tier of beams and the ground (no basement).

creepage. The travel of electrolyte up the surface of electrodes or other parts of the cell above the level of the main body of electrolyte.

creeping. An evaporation of the electrolyte of primary cells which results in crystals being left on the sides of the jar previously wetted by the solution, the action being very marked when the solution is a saturated one.

creep of belt. A term applied to the slipping of a belt.

crest value (peak value). The maximum absolute value of a function when such a maximum exists.

crimp wire splice. A tool that makes a reliable electrical splice or connection by mashing a metal sleeve over the wires to be joined.

critical current. That strength of an electric current required to bring about some special effect in electric operation.

crooke's effect. An effect obtained in high vacuum tubes, resulting from motions peculiar to heated or electrified molecules when in high state of radiation.

cross. Any accidental contact between electric wires or conductors.

cross arms. A support for insulators upon which conductors are strung and attached to a pole.

cross current. A current which when two separately driven alternators are coupled in parallel and one lags behind the other in phase, flows for a brief time from the leading to the lagging alternator.

cross section. A cutting or piece of something cut off at right angles to an axis. The cross-sectional area is 100% of the cross section.

crowbar circuit. A circuit that causes an electrical overload to exist in the event certain other operations are not completed. The overload condition in turn causes an overcurrent or thermal device to function.

crow foot. A zinc electrode, suggesting a crow's foot in shape; used in a gravity cell.

crow's foot. A metallic bracket resembling a crow's foot in shape, sometimes used in the mounting of a light fixture to a box.

crusher. A term sometimes applied to a motor used to reduce the pressure on a feeder line by absorbing the extra voltage, when that line requires less pressure than that delivered by the main dynamo.

cube. A rectangular solid, measuring the same lineally in the three directions of length, breadth, and thickness. Its contents are equal to the product of the lineal measurement of each dimension, hence the third power of a number is termed its cube, as it represents the product of three factors, each equal to the stated number.

cube tap. When plugged into a receptacle outlet provides an additional 3 outlets. Also called straight blade tap and adapter, add-a-tap, and 3-way prong adapter.

cubic measure. This measure is used to find the volume or amount of space within the boundary surfaces of a body.

cubic yard. The customary unit for measuring excavations, embankments, also concrete and masonry. It is a volume equal to that of a six sided figure or cube, each edge of which measures one yard or three feet.

current. The movement of electrons through a conductor; measured in amperes, milliamperes, and microamperes.

current, electric. The flow of electrical energy along a conductor from the higher to the lower of two points having different pressures. The "flow" is simply the effort to equalize the two pressures just as water runs from a higher to lower level, or pressure; the current may be maintained by preserving a constant difference of pressure between the two connected points.

current density. The strength of current which flows in any part of a circuit divided by the cross section area of that section of the circuit.

current, fault. Fault current is a current that results from the loss of insulation between conductors or between a conductor and ground.

current-limiting fuse. A fuse that, when it is melted by a current within its specified current-limiting range, abruptly introduces a high arc voltage to reduce the current magnitude and duration. (CL fuse)

current-limiting overcurrent protective device. A device which, when interrupting currents in its current-limiting range, will reduce the current flowing in the faulted circuit to a magnitude substantially less than that obtainable in the same circuit if the device were replaced with a solid conductor having comparable impedance.

current meter. An instrument for measuring the strength of an electric current. For example, an ammeter is a current meter, showing by direct reading, the number of amperes of current flowing through a circuit.

current relay. A switching relay that operates on a predetermined amount of electrical flow (or lack of current flow).

current strength. The amount of electricity that passes any cross section of a circuit in a second of time.

current transformer. An instrument transformer with a primary winding in series with a current-carrying conductor and secondary winding connected to a meter or device which is actuated by conductor current and current changes. Sometimes called a "CT" or "doughnut".

curtain wall. Nonbearing wall between piers or columns for the enclosure of the structure; not supported at each story.

cut in. To insert a conducting appliance or medium into an electric circuit; to switch on.

cut lines of force. A conductor, forming part of an electric circuit, cuts lines of force when it moves across a magnetic field in such a manner as to alter the number of magnetic lines of force which are embraced by the circuit.

cutout. To take out a conducting or medium from an electric circuit; to switch off. An electrical device to interrupt the flow of current through any particular apparatus or instrument, either automatically or by hand.

cutout box. An enclosure designed for surface mounting and having swinging doors or covers secured directly to and telescoping with the walls of the box proper.

curve of sines. A curve which represents at continuous successive positions the successive values of the sines of a progressively varying angle.

cycle. A complete reversal of alternating current, passing through a complete set of changes or motions in opposite directions, from a rise to maximum, return to zero, rise to maximum in the other direction, and another return to zero. One complete positive and one complete negative alternation of a current or voltage.

cyclometer. An instrument for registering the number of revolutions made, or distance measured, by a wheel or other rotating body.

D

damper. A metallic tube which may be pressed over the core of an induction coil to reduce the induction and lessen the currents of the secondary circuit.

damper winding. An amortisseur winding.

dampproof. Having an insulation saturated with some nonabsorbent material such as asphalt compound.

damp location. Partially protected locations under canopies, marquees, roofed open porches, and like locations, and interior locations subject to moderate degrees of moisture, such as some basements, barns, and cold storage warehouses.

daraf. The unit of elastance or reciprocal of electrostatic capacity.

d'Arsonval galvanometer. A very sensitive, irregular or deadbeat galvanometer in which the indicating coil is suspended in the field of a powerful horseshoe magnet; the invention of A. d'Arsonval. Its operation depends upon the principle that if a flat coil of wire be suspended with its axis perpendicular to a strong magnetic field, it will be deflected whenever a current of electricity passes through it. Its sensitivity depends upon the strength of the field of the permanent magnet, the number of turns in the suspended coil, and the tortion of the wires by which it is suspended. This type of galvanometer is used for general laboratory work as it is not easily affected by changes in the magnetic field.

dead. Free from any electric connection to a source of potential difference and from electric charge. The term is used only with reference to current-carrying parts that are sometimes alive.

deadbeat. A term applied to instruments having indicators which prevent tedious swinging back and forth after deflection, by being heavily damped so that they come to rest quickly.

53

dead end. The ends of circuit wires which are connected to supports, but do not carry an electric load. The termination of a line wire on an insulator.

dead-end guy. An installation of line or anchor guys to hold the pole at the end of a line.

dead front. Without live parts exposed to a person on the operating side of the equipment.

dead-front mounting. A method of mounting in which a protective barrier is interposed between all live parts and the operator, and all exposed operating parts are insulated or grounded. The barrier is usually grounded metal.

dead man. A pole support consisting of a heavy wooden bar terminating in a broad U-shaped iron fork, designed to prop a pole while being raised; a butt prop.

dead metal part. A metal or other electrically conductive part, accessible or inaccessible, that is not conductively connected to a live part.

dead point of armature. A relation of a motor armature to the field such that it cannot start under the action of the driving current.

debug. To examine or test a procedure, routine, or equipment for the purpose of detecting and correcting errors.

decelerating relay. A relay that functions automatically to maintain the armature current or voltage within limits, when decelerating from speeds above base speed, by controlling the excitation of the motor field.

decelerating time. The time in seconds for a change of speed from one specified speed to a lower specified speed while decelerating under specified conditions.

deci. A Latin prefix often used with a physical unit to designate a quantity one-tenth of that unit.

deciampere. A unit of electric current equal to the tenth part of an ampere.

decibel. (a) Technically, a measure of relative power levels. (b) A measure of the loudness of a bell, siren, horn, or other noise. (c) The strength of an audio signal.

decimal fraction or decimal. A fraction whose denominator is 10 or a power of 10. It is usually written without the denominator, the number of ciphers in the denominator being indicated by the number of places occupied by the number preceded if necessary by ciphers, and placed after a point or period called the "decimal point".

deepwell pump. An electrically-driven pump located at the low point to discharge the water accumulation to the surface.

defeat. Circumvention or bypassing of an alarm system, rendering it or a portion of it inoperative.

definite-purpose motor. Any motor designed, listed, and offered in standard ratings with standard operating characteristics or mechanical construction for use under service conditions other than usual or for use on a particular type of application such as elevators, cranes, oil-burner motors, etc.

definite time. A qualifying term applied to any relay indicating that there is purposely introduced a delay in action, which delay remains substantially constant regardless of the magnitude of the operating quantities. For quantities slightly above the minimum operating value, the delay may be inverse.

deflection. The distance or angle by which one line departs from another.

degree day. A unit based on temperature difference and time used to specify the normal heating load in winter. For one day there exists as many degree days as there are degrees F difference in temperature between the average outside air temperature, taken over a 24-hour period, and a temperature of 65 degrees F.

degree, electrical. An angle equal to 1/360 of the angle between consecutive field poles of like polarity in an electrical machine. One electrical degree is equal to 1 (pair of poles) part of a mechanical degree.

degrees. The circumference of every circle is supposed to be divided into 360 equal parts, called degrees; thus, a degree is 1/360th of the circumference of any circle.

dehumidifier. An air cooler used for lowering the moisture content of the air passing through it. An absorption or absorption device for removing moisture from the air.

deka. A Greek prefix often used with a physical unit to designate a quantity ten times as great.

delay. The amount of time by which an event is retarded.

delay relay. A relay having an assured time interval between energization and pickup or between de-energization and dropout.

delta connection. The connection of the circuits in a three phase system in which the terminal connections are triangular like the Greek letter delta. The delta connection will stand 1.732 as much current as the Y connection, but will give only .577 as much voltage.

delta high-leg. Generally the center phase. It's to be colored orange or tagged. The high-leg voltage to neutral on a 230/115v system would be 199 volts.

delta-three-phase system. The triangular connection applied to a three-phase system, so that the transmission wires are joined to the three corners of a triangle.

delta-Y connection. In this method the primaries are connected in delta grouping and the secondaries in star grouping.

demagnetization. The process of removing magnetism from a magnetic substance.

demand factor. The ratio of the maximum demand of a system, or part of a system, to the total connected load of a system or the part of the system under consideration.

demand meter. A device which indicates or records the demand or maximum demand. Demand meters measure a quantity which is composed of an electrical factor and a time factor.

denominator. That part of a fraction which expresses the number of parts into which the unit or number is divided.

densimeter. A device used to determine the specific gravity or relative density of a substance. Usually called a hydrometer.

density, electric. The quantity of electricity on a unit of area at any part of a charged body.

density of current. The amount of electric current which passes in any part of a circuit as compared with the area of cross section of that part of the circuit.

density of flux. The number of lines of force per unit area of cross section in a plane at right angles to the lines of force.

denuder. That portion of an electrolytic cell of the mercury type in which the alkali metal is separated from the mercury.

depolarizer. A substance employed in some types of cell to combine with the hydrogen which would otherwise be set free at the positive electrode and cause polarization.

derived current. A current which passes through a shunt or derived circuit.

derrick. An apparatus consisting of a mast or equivalent members held at the top by guys or braces, with or without a boom, for use with a hoisting mechanism and operating ropes.

design voltage. The voltage at which the device is designed to draw rated watts input.

detector. Any device that senses the presence of an intruder, an intrusion attempt, fire, smoke, or any other dangerous or undesirable condition.

deteriorate. To grow worse in quality or value.

deterrent. Anything which discourages. The presence of an alarm should, in the first place, discourage a potential intruder from attempting to break in.

dew point. The temperature of the atmosphere at which dew would form or condensation would occur.

deviation. Any departure from a desired or expected value or pattern.

device. A unit of an electrical system which is intended to carry but not utilize electric energy.

diagonal. A line joining two opposite angles of a quadrilateral figure, and dividing it into two parts.

diagram. A skeleton geometrical drawing, illustrating the principles of application of a mechanism.

dial. A graduated circular plate upon which anything is indicated by a needle; as in a voltmeter.

diamagnetic material. A material whose relative permeability is less than unity.

diameter of a circle. A straight line passing through its center and terminating at both ends in the circumference.

diamond winding. One which is made up of similarly shaped overlapping coils which have V-shaped coil ends, so bent that approximately half of each coil is on one side of the plane of the coil side and the other half of each coil end is on the other side of the plane of the coil side. The diamond winding is the prevailing type.

dielectric. A medium or substance in which a potential difference establishes an electric field which is subsequently recoverable as electric energy. An insulator; a term that refers to the insulating material between the plates of a capacitor.

dielectric heating. The heating of a nominally insulated material in an alternating electric field due to its internal losses.

dielectric strength. The maximum voltage that the dielectric can withstand without rupture.

differential. The difference between the cut-in and cut-out settings of a control.

diffuser. A piece of equipment to redirect or scatter the light from a source, primarily by the process of diffuse transmission.

diffusing bulb. An incandescent lamp in which a frosting or coating makes the lamp bulb translucent, so the light appears to come from its entire area, masking the high brilliancy of the filament.

diffusing panel. A translucent material covering the lamps in a luminaire in order to reduce the brightness by distributing the flux over an extended area.

dihedral angle. The angle formed by the intersection of two planes.

dilatometer. An instrument for determining the amount of expansion a liquid undergoes when heated.

dimmer. A resistance inserted in a lighting circuit for shunting or by-passing a variable portion of the current, thus "dimming" the lights in the circuit.

diode. A two-electrode electron tube containing an anode and a cathode. Diodes are used as rectifiers and detectors.

diphase. A term sometimes used for two-phase. The latter is preferable.

direct current. A unidirectional current. It may be constant or periodically fluctuating, as rectified alternating current.

direct current generator. An objectionable term for a dynamo.

direct drive. A transmission in which the prime mover or driver is connected to a machine without any form or gearing between them.

direct EMF. Also termed "direct voltage"; EMF that does not change in polarity and has a constant value.

direction of current flow. It is arbitrarily assumed that current flows from a positive terminal to a negative terminal; however electrons, as in a vacuum tube, actually flow in the opposite direction.

direct lighting. Lighting involving luminaires that distribute 90 to 100 percent of the emitted light in the general direction of the surface to be illuminated.

direct spark ignition. A method by which the main-burner gas is ignited by a spark across the ports of the main burner rather than lighting a pilot burner. The spark is generated by a high voltage transformer in the ignition circuit.

disarm. To turn off an alarm when opening the protected premises for business.

discharge. (a) The effort to overcome differences of voltage which takes place between two charged terminals when a connection is made between them. (b) To bring about an electric discharge by connecting two charged points. (c) The removal of a charge from the surface of any charged conductor by connecting it with earth, or another conductor. (d) The removal of a charge by means of a stream of electrified air particles. Examples: Discharge of a storage battery, discharge of a capacitor, lightning discharge of a thundercloud.

discharge current. The surge current that flows through the lightning arrester after a sparkover.

disconnecting means. A device, or group of devices, or other means by which the conductors of a circuit can be disconnected from their source of supply.

displacement current. The apparent flow of charge "through" a dielectric such as in a capacitor; represented by buildup and/or decay of an electric field.

disruptive discharge. A rapid and large current increase through an insulator due to insulation failure.

dissipation. Loss of electric energy as heat.

dissipation function. A function signifying the rate at which the passage of an electric current through a conductor produces heat.

distributed capacity. The capacity distributed between conducting elements; distinguished from capacity concentrated in a condenser.

distributing center. A central point of electric distribution.

diversity factor. The ratio between the simultaneous demand of a number of individual services for a specified period, and the sum of the individual demands of those services for the same period. This definition is expressed as a fraction or as a percentage and is never greater than one.

divided circuit. If a circuit is divided into two branches at one point, uniting again at another, the current will also be divided, part flowing through one branch and part through the other. The relative strength of current in the two branches will be proportional to their conductivities.

divider, voltage. A tapped resistor or series arrangement of resistors, sometimes with movable contacts, providing a desired IR drop.

door cord. A very flexible, sturdy, jacketed wire used to carry an alarm circuit onto a door, window, or other movable object to connect to the foil on other protective devices.

double break switch. One which breaks a circuit at two contacts along the same wire. Distinguish between double break and double pole switch.

double connector. A binding screw suitable for connecting the ends of two wires.

double-faced tape. Fabric tape finished on both sides with a rubber or synthetic compound.

double filament lamp. An incandescent lamp having two filaments usually of different lengths and of different resistance. The short filament is of very low candlepower and is not in circuit with the longer filament.

double hung window. A type of window popular in older construction. The lower sash can be raised and the upper sash can be lowered.

double pole. Switch or device connected to both sides of a circuit or controlling both sides of a circuit.

double pole switch. One which simultaneously opens or closes two separate circuits or both sides of the same circuit.

double-strength glass. Sheet glass that is one-eighth inch thick (single-strength glass is one-tenth inch thick).

double throw switch. One which connects one circuit terminal to either of two other circuit terminals.

double winding. An armature winding consisting of two independent insulated coils, each joined to alternate segments of the commutator, thereby dividing the current between the coils, and reducing the inductance in the circuit.

doughnut. A term used for a current transformer (CT).

down conductor. The vertical portion of a run of a conductor that ends at the ground.

down lead. The wire connection from the aerial to the receiving set. Usually called the lead in.

downlight. A small direct lighting unit which can be recessed, surface mounted, or suspended.

down time. The period during which a system or device is not operating due to internal failures, scheduled shut down, or servicing.

drehstrom. A German term for a rotating or rotary current.

drill mount. Generally refers to a contact that can simply be mounted in a drilled hole.

drip loop. In house wiring, a loop extending downward made at the point where a wire enters a building. The lower end of the loop is below the entrance point. Water gathering on the wire will drip from the loop.

dripproof. So constructed or protected that successful operation is not interfered with when falling drops of liquid strike or enter the enclosure at any angle from 0 to 15 degrees from the downward verticle unless otherwise specified.

dripproof apparatus. Apparatus so constructed or protected that its successful operation is not interfered with when subjected to falling moisture or dirt.

drop. The voltage drop developed across a resistor due to current flowing through it.

drop box. A box containing pendant or flush mounted receptacles attached to a multiconductor cable via strain relief, or a multi-pole connector.

drop cord. Twisted insulated wires extending from a socket, rosette, or outlet box to a lamp, electric cooking utensil, or other current consuming device.

dropout fuse. A fuse in which the fuseholder or fuse unit automatically drops into an open position after the fuse has interrupted the circuit.

dropout relay. A term for contact operation (opening or closing) as a relay just departs from pickup.

dropout voltage. The voltage or point at which the pull of the electromagnet is not strong enough to keep the armature seated.

drop, voltage. An IR voltage between two specified points in an electric circuit.

drum. A spool or reel for carrying coils of wire.

drum controller. One which utilizes a drum switch as the main switching element.

dry battery. An assembly of dry cells connected as a unit. This term is often and very objectionably applied to a single cell.

dry-bulb temperature. The temperature indicated on a dry bulb thermometer. It indicates the heat of the air and water vapor mixture.

dry cable. A term sometimes applied to a conducting cable composed of wires contained within a lead sheath and separated from each other by air and paper; a dry core cable.

dry cell. A primary cell consisting of two elements, usually zinc and carbon, and a liquid electrolyte.

dry location. A location not normally subject to dampness or wetness. A location classified as dry may be temporarily subject to dampness or wetness, as in the case of a building under construction.

dry transformer. A transformer employing air instead of oil as the cooling agent.

drywall. Interior wall construction consisting of plaster boards, wood paneling, or plywood nailed directly to the studs without application of plaster.

dual control. A term applied to signal appliances provided with two authorized methods of operation.

dual operation. An elevator control system in which push button operation is combined with manual operation in the same car.

duck tape. Tape of heavy cotton fabric, such as duck or drill, which may be impregnated with an asphalt, rubber, or synthetic compound.

duct. One of the channels in an underground conduit in which wires or cables may be run.

duct bank. An arrangement of conduit providing one or more continuous ducts between two points.

duct, channel. A device (other than a tie, strap, or clamp) providing continuous support for lengths of wire or cable, and consisting of a main channel body and closure lid. A duct and channel may also position (secure) the wire or cable to a surface or frame.

duct fittings. In underfloor wiring, since the service extension assembly and service fittings frequently occupy positions under desks or in footspace, they are purposely designed to be kickproof.

duct rodding. The threading of a duct by means of a jointed rod or suitable design for the purpose of pulling in the cable pulling rope, mandrel, or the cable itself.

dumbwaiter. A hoisting and lowering mechanism equipped with a car that moves in guides in a substantially vertical direction, the capacity of which does not exceed 500 pounds, and which is used exclusively for carrying materials.

dummy terminals. Extra terminals that do not connect to an electrical function on a control. They are sometimes provided for wiring convenience.

duplex cable. A cable composed of two insulated stranded conductors twisted together. Duplex cables may or may not have a common insulating covering.

duress switch. A special type of key switch that can be turned in either of two directions or with two different keys.

dustproof. So constructed or protected that the accumulation of dust will not interfere with successful operation.

dust tight. So constructed that dust will not enter the enclosing case under specified test conditions.

dutchman. A piece "fitted in" to restore a worn part or to hide a defect.

duty. A statement of loads including no-load and rest and de-energized periods, to which the machine or apparatus is subjected including their duration and sequence in time.

duty cycle. The time interval occupied by a device on intermittent duty in starting, running, stopping, and idling.

dwelling unit. One or more rooms for the use of one or more persons as a housekeeping unit with space for eating, living, and sleeping, and permanent provisions for cooking and sanitation.

dynamic brakes. In electric traction or electric elevators, a method of braking in which the motor is run as a dynamo with a resistance load, thus introducing a reverse force which tends to stop the car.

dynamics. That branch of mechanics which treats the action of forces producing motion in bodies.

dynamo. A machine for converting mechanical energy into electrical energy by means of electromagnetic induction.

dynamometer. An instrument used for measuring power.

dynamotor. A combination dynamo and motor having either two armatures or one armature with two windings and one magnetic field. The motor element is used to drive the dynamo with a pressure either higher or lower than that received at the motor terminals.

67

E

E. Symbol for voltage.

ear. An insulating device for supporting a trolley wire from the suspension span wire; a trolley ear.

earth. The ground considered as a medium for completing an electric circuit.

earth circuit. An electric circuit which is completed by the use of the ground as a part of the circuit; a ground circuit.

earth connection. A connection made between any electrical circuit or instrument and the earth, also called a ground connection.

earth currents. Electric currents flowing through the ground due to a natural difference of pressure.

earthenware conduit. A conduit for underground or other concealed wiring, made of glazed earthenware or clay.

earthed neutral. In transformer practice, the grounding of the middle or neutral point of the secondary winding of the transformer in order to reduce fire risk in case the primary should become accidentally grounded; usually called the grounded neutral.

earth magnetic state. That condition of the earth by virtue of which it possesses magnetic attraction. The intensity of the earth's magnetic force at any place is the force with which a magnet pole of unit strength is attracted.

earth pressure. The electric pressure of the earth considered as a large conducting sphere. This is due to a positive charge residing near its surface, but as a positive charge generates an equal negative charge, the earth's pressure, due to both charges, equals zero.

earth return. The earth considered as the return path of an electric circuit; ground return.

eburin. An insulating compound used especially for strain insulators.

eccentric. Not having the same center, deviating from a circular path, located elsewhere than at the center.

eccentricity. The distance from the center of a figure or revolving body to the axis about which it turns. In the eccentric used in engineering, this distance is equal to one-half the throw. The mistake of considering the throw as equal to the eccentricity should be avoided.

eddy-current braking. A form of electric braking in which the energy to be dissipated is converted into heat by eddy currents produced in a metallic mass.

eddy current loss. The iron core of a transformer acts as a closed conductor in which small pressure of different value are induced in different parts by the alternating field, giving rise to eddy currents. Energy is thus consumed by these currents which is wasted in heating the iron, reducing the efficiency of the transformer. This loss is reduced by laminating the core.

eddy currents. Induced electric currents occurring when a solid metallic mass is rotated in a magnetic field. They consume a large amount of energy and often cause harmful rise in temperature. The pole pieces, field magnet cores, and armatures of dynamos and motors are especially subject to these currents.

Edison base. The standard screw base used for light bulbs.

Edison, Thomas Alva. Born in 1847, died 1931. An American inventor famous for his experiments in applied electricity.

Edison three-wire system. A system of electrical distribution employing two dynamos joined in series and connected at their free terminals to the positive and negative mains, respectively, between which a neutral wire, usually smaller than the mains, is introduced and joined to the junction of the dynamos. The object of this system is to reduce the amount of copper required.

effective current. The value of alternating current that will cause the same heating effect as a given value of direct current.

effective value. The effective value of a sine-wave AC current or voltage is equal to 0.707 of peak (maximum). Also called the "root-mean-square (rms) value".

effective volts. That pressure which is available for driving electricity around a circuit, or for doing work. Distinguish between virtual and effective volts and amperes. An effective current is that indicated by an ammeter when the current is in phase with the pressure.

efficiency. The ratio of energy output to energy input, expressed as a percentage.

efficiency of motor. The relation of the electric power discharged at a motor pulley to that which is furnished at its terminals.

egg insulator. An egg shaped strain insulator.

elbow. A pipe fitting, consisting of a short bend through various angles. When it is necessary to change the direction of a pipe line to any of several standard and special angles, elbows are used.

electrepeter. An instrument for changing the direction of an electric current; a pole changer.

electrical codes. A compilation of rules and regulations covering electric installations.

electrical horsepower. 746 watts.

electrical units. In the practical system, electrical units comprise the volt, the ampere, the ohm, the watt, the watt-hour, the coulomb, the henry, the mho, the joule, and the farad.

electric circuit. The path (whether metallic or nonmetallic) of an electric current.

electric contact. The junction of conducting parts permitting current to flow.

electric degree. 1/360 part of a cycle. In a two pole elementary alternator the cycle is completed in one revolution; for a four pole machine, in one-half revolution, etc. One electrical degree is equal to 1 (pair of poles) part of a mechanical degree.

electric-discharge lamp. A lamp in which light is produced by the passage of an electric current through a vapor or gas. Neon, sodium, mercury, fluorescent, etc. are electric-discharge lamps.

electric eye. A photoelectric cell. In noctovision if an object is illuminated by infrared rays it can be clearly seen by the "electric eye" but is invisible to the human eye.

electric field. A vector field of electric field strength or of flux density.

electric generator. A machine that transforms mechanical power into electric power.

electric gradient. The rapidity of increase or decrease of voltage.

electric hygrometer. An instrument for indicating, by electric means, the humidity of the ambient atmosphere.

electrician. A person who is versed in the knowledge of electricity.

electricity. The name is given to an invisible agent known only by its effects and manifestations, as shown in electrical phenomena. Electricity, no matter how produced, is believed to be one and the same thing.

electric motor. A machine that transforms electric power into mechanical power.

electric reset relay. A relay that is so constructed that it remains in the picked-up condition even after the input quantity is removed; an independent electric input is required to reset the relay.

electric sign. A fixed, stationary, or portable self-contained, electrically illuminated, utilization equipment with words or symbols designed to convey information or attract attention.

electric strength (dielectric strength). The maximum potential gradient that the material (insulation) can withstand without rupture.

electric switch lock. An electric lock used to prevent the operation of a switch or a switch movement until the lock is released.

electrocalorimetry. The operation of measuring the heat developed by an electric current in a conductor or circuit.

electrochemical meter. An electric meter which measures the current by the amount of chemical change it causes in a metallic solution; an electrolytic meter.

electrocution. The destruction of life by means of electric current.

electrochemistry. The production or separation of chemical elements and compounds by the action of electric currents.

electrode. A conducting substance through which electric current enters or leaves in devices that provide electrical control or energy conversion.

electrodes. (a) In electrolysis, the terminal plates in the bath; the plate by which the current enters the solution is called the anode and that by which the current leaves is called the cathode. (b) In a primary cell, the plates immersed in the exciting fluid or electrolyte. (c) In arc lighting the carbons which form the terminals to the arc.

electroendosmosis. Is the phenomenon which causes the "green goo ooze" often encountered on polyvinylchloride (PVC) insulated conductors of direct current circuits in wet locations. The fact that PVC is microporous allows moisture to be transferred by osmosis from the environment through the insulation to the DC circuit conductor. This does not seem to occur with rubber insulation.

electrolier. A fixture for supporting a cluster of incandescent electric lamps.

electrolysis. The decomposition of a chemical compound in solution, called the electrolyte, into its constituent elements, called ions, by the passage of an electric current through it.

electrolyte. A substance that provides electrical conduction when dissolved. An electrolyte may be in the form of either a liquid or a paste. (usually in water).

electrolytic cell. A vessel containing an electrolyte, in which electrolysis is carried on.

electrolytic conductor. Flow of electric charges to and from electrodes in an electrolytic solution.

electrolyze. To electrically separate or decompose.

electromagnet. A magnet produced by passing an electric current through an insulated wire conductor coiled around a core of soft iron, as in the fields of a dynamo or motor.

electromagnetic induction. A process of generation of emf by movement of magnetic flux which cuts an electrical conductor.

73

electromagnetic inertia. A term applied to the self-inductance of a current.

electrometry. The art or practice of electrical measurement.

electromotive force (EMF). An energy-charge relation that results in electric pressure (voltage), which produces or tends to produce charge flow.

electron. The smallest charge of negative electricity known.

electronics. The science and art dealing with the flow of electricity or electrons through vacuums and gases confined within the envelopes of tubes or tanks.

electropathy. The use of electricity in the treatment of disease; electrotherapeutics.

electrophore. A device for obtaining static electricity by inductance; an electrophorus.

electroplating. The process of depositing a layer or coating of a rarer metal upon the surface of a baser, or of a metal upon any conducting surface by electrolysis.

electropneumatic. Relating to the action of compressed air in combination with electricity.

electropolar. Having one end or surface positively electrified and the other negatively electrified.

electroscope. An instrument for detecting whether a body be electrified or not, and indicating also whether the electrification be positive or negative.

electrose. A trade name for a substance manufactured into high power transmission insulators. It has a brown, smooth polished surface, is very strong, does not absorb moisture, and possesses good insulating properties.

electrostatic field. The region occupied by electrostatic lines of force in the vicinity of an electrostatically charged body.

electrostatics. A branch of electrical science dealing with the laws of electricity at rest.

electrotherapeutics. The study of the physiological effect of electrical current passing through the body.

electrothermal meter. A term sometimes applied to the hot wire ammeter or voltmeter which operates on the principle that if an electric current passes through a constant resistance, the heat generated must be equal to the square of the current.

electrothermics. The branch of science and technology that deals with the direct transformations of electric energy and heat.

element. A substance which the chemist cannot, by any of the means under his control, resolve into two or more simpler substances. A mass composed of atoms all of which are of one kind. There are two kinds of elements; the metals, of which there are 73 and the nonmetals, of which there are 18.

element, bimetallic. An element formed of two metals having different coefficients of thermal expansion, such as used in temperature indicating and controlling devices.

elevation. Drawing showing the projection of a building on a vertical plane.

elevator. A car for passengers or freight arranged to move vertically.

elongation. The amplitude of the angle described by a measuring instrument which starts at zero and ends at a maximum value. With galvanometers, elongation shows the value of current passing in the galvanometer.

embedded cable. Protective wiring set in a solid medium, such as concrete or plastic, that will open or cross, or both open and cross, the protective circuit if an opening, manhole or handhole size, is made through the medium.

embedded coils. Armature coils wound in grooves or channels sunk beneath the surface of an armature.

emergency button. A pushbutton switch connected to a local bell alarm system so that momentarily pushing the button will immediately sound the bell, even if the protective loop part of the system is turned off at the time.

emergency lighting. Lighting designed to supply illumination essential to the safety of life and property in the event of failure of the normal supply.

emergency service. An additional service intended only for use under emergency conditions.

emergency signal. Audible or visual signal that requires immediate action.

emery. This is a dark colored granular variety of corundum, which is the hardest substance found, next to the diamond.

encapsulant. Transparent insulating material enclosing the cells and cell interconnects.

encapsulated. A machine in which one or more of the windings is completely encased by molded insulation.

enclosed. Surrounded by a case, housing, fence, or walls which will prevent persons from accidentally contacting energized parts.

enclosed relay. A relay that has both coil and contacts protected from the surrounding medium.

enclosure. The case or housing of apparatus, or the fence or walls surrounding an installation, to prevent personnel from accidentally contacting energized parts, or to protect the equipment from physical damage.

end cap. A cover intended to close the open end of a track.

end cells. The cells near the end of a storage battery which are cut in and out of circuit by means of the end cell switches, in order to keep the voltage constant at the battery terminals.

end to end joint. A method of joining two lengths of wire by bringing the ends into close contact and soldering or welding them together; commonly called the "butt-joint".

energized part. A part, at some point potential, with respect to another part, or to earth.

energy. The amount of physical work a system is capable of doing. Electrical energy is measured in watt-seconds, or the product of power and time.

energy current. In an alternating current circuit, the working or active component of the current in phase with the volts; the energy component, as distinguished from the wattless component.

energy efficiency. The efficiency of an electric machine measured in watt hours or kilowatt hours; the watt hour efficiency.

energy, electric. The work done in a circuit or conductor by a current passing through it. When a current flows from one point to another, there is a drop in voltage and work is accomplished. The amount of this work is measured by the quantity of electricity that flows, multiplied by the difference of voltage under which it flows; its unit is the joule.

energy, maximum. The test condition under which, in a specified maximum time (1/2 cycle), the maximum amount of heat possible is generated in the fuse before clearing.

energy meter. A name sometimes given to the wattmeter.

engage. To interlock with another part; as the teeth of geared wheels with each other, or a rack with its pinion.

engineer, electrical. A person versed in the science of electricity and skilled in electric practice; usually one who has had special training in an engineering school and obtained the degree E.E.

entrefer. The open space between the face of the pole piece of a dynamo and the surface of the armature; the air gap.

environment. The universe within which the system must operate. All the elements over which the designer has no control and that affect the system or its inputs and outputs.

Epstein hysteresis tester. A device for measuring hysteresis and eddy current loss in which an AC wattmeter is used.

equalizing current. When compound wound dynamos are operated in parallel, the current carried by the equalizer bar to insure uniform distribution among the series coils of the machines.

equator of magnet. A line assumed to encircle a magnet at a point where there is no polarity or attractive power; a line passing through the neutral points. In a bar magnet it lies midway between the poles.

equidistant. Situated at equal distances from the same point or thing.

equipment. A general term including material, fittings, devices, appliances, fixtures, apparatus, and the like used as a part of, or in connection with, an electrical installation.

equipment ground. A ground connection to noncurrent-carrying metal parts of a wiring installation or of electric equipment, or both.

equipment grounding conductor. The conductor used to connect the noncurrent-carrying metal parts of equipment, raceways, and other enclosures to the system grounded conductor and/or the grounding electrode conductor at the service equipment or at the source of a separately derived system.

equipment, service. A circuit breaker or switches and fuses with their accessories, installed near the point of entry of service conductors to a building.

equivalent conductivity. A conductivity equal to the sum of other conductivities in an electric circuit.

equivalent resistance. A resistance equal to the sum of other resistances in an electric circuit.

equivolt. A term proposed for the mechanical energy of one volt pressure exerted under conditions through one equivalent of chemical action in grains.

erickson. A coupling used to connect two sections of rigid conduit when neither section can be turned; a union.

erosion. Deterioration by the abrasive action of fluids, usually accelerated by the presence of solid particles of matter in suspension.

escutcheon. A protective or ornamental shield around a keyhole.

eudiometer. A graduated glass tube, used in the analysis of gases, for measuring their volume.

evaporation, electric. The evaporation of a liquid and volatilization of a solid, accelerated by the influence of negative electricity.

evolute connections. Fork shaped strips used to connect bars at different positions on the armature. Used with evolute winding.

excitation. The magnetizing of the field magnets of dynamos, alternators, etc., by the passage of a current through the winding of the magnets. The exciting current is obtained either from the machine itself in self-exciting dynamos, or from an outside source in separately excited dynamos.

exciter. An auxiliary generator for supplying electrical energy to the field of another electrical machine.

exit light. A complete, enclosed unit assembly arranged for permanent connection, with one or more lamps that illuminate an integral legend "EXIT" upon failure of the normal power supply. An exit light may have an automatic load control device and may be provided with a storage battery. If a battery is used, a means for charging the battery is included.

exothermic. Characterized or formed with evolution of heat.

expansion bolt. Bolt with a casing arranged to wedge the bolt into a masonry wall to provide an anchorage.

expansion joint. A fitting intended to compensate for linear thermal expansion of a span of rigid conduit.

exploring coil. A coil wound around a magnetic circuit for the purpose of measuring any change in flux through the magnetic circuit by means of the quantity of electricity sent through an external circuit of known resistance. This quantity can be measured either by a ballistic galvanometer or by a flux meter.

explosionproof apparatus. Apparatus enclosed in a case that is capable of withstanding an explosion of a specified gas or vapor which may occur within it and of preventing the ignition of a specified gas or vapor surrounding the enclosure by sparks, flashes, or explosion of the gas or vapor within, and which operates at such an external temperature that a surrounding flammable atmosphere will not be ignited thereby.

exposed (as applied to live parts). Capable of being inadvertently touched or approached nearer than a safe distance by a person. It is applied to parts not suitably guarded, isolated, or insulated.

exposed (as applied to wiring methods). On or attached to the surface or behind panels designed to allow access.

expulsion fuse. One designed to be blown in a confined space such as an explosion chamber. A fuse blown under such a condition has the property of quickly opening the circuit and projecting the arc from the open end of the chamber.

extension cord. An assembly of a flexible cord with an attachment plug on one end and a cord connector on the other.

extensometer. An apparatus for measuring the expansion or contraction of metal bars affected by the temperature or by strain.

external. The outside surface of the enclosure or the plane drawn across the open face of a reflector, but excluding guards and minor projections such as lamp bulb tips, handles, and control knobs.

external circuit. The portion of an electric circuit which is outside of the source of current.

externally operable. Capable of being operated without exposing the operator to contact with live parts.

external resistance. The resistance existing in an electric circuit outside of the dynamo or battery source of the current.

81

extra currents. A current of brief duration caused by electromagnetic induction, arising when a circuit is suddenly opened or closed; a self-induced current.

extraction of metals. The process of separating metals from their ores by electrolysis.

F

FD box. A cast iron box used with steel conduit. The "F" is for a fitting box. The "D" is for deep.

FS box. A cast iron box used with steel conduit. The "F" is for a fitting box. The "S" is for shallow.

factor. One of two or more quantities which, when multiplied together, produce a given quantity.

Fahrenheit. The thermometer scale in general use in the United States. On this scale 32 degrees represents the freezing point of ice and 212 degrees the boiling point of water at sea level. It is commonly abbreviated Fahr. or F.

failure. The termination of the ability of an item to perform its required function.

fall of pressure. A drop or decrease of electrical pressure in a circuit due to resistance in the conductor. In a wire of uniform resistance, the fall of pressure follows the rule that the electrical pressure along a conductor through which a given current flows, falls directly, as the resistance increases; that is, the voltage is inversely proportional to the resistance. Also called voltage drop.

false zero. A zero on a galvanometer scale considered to be at the value of the deflection obtained before the action of forces impressed in the measurement.

fan. An air-moving device comprising a wheel or blade, and housing or oriface plate.

fan, ceiling suspended. A fan intended to be mounted to a ceiling outlet box or ceiling building structure, and whose blades rotate below the ceiling. Called a paddle fan.

fan control. A switch used to cycle the indoor fan on and off in response to the temperature inside the heat exchanger.

farad. Practical unit of electrostatic capacity in the electromagnetic system. A condenser is said to have a capacity of one farad if it will absorb one coulomb (that is, one ampere per second), of electricity when subjected to a pressure of one volt. The unit of capacitance.

Faraday effect. A discovery made by Faraday that a wave of light polarized in a certain plane can be turned about by the influence of a magnet so that the vibrations occur in a different plane.

Faraday's discovery. In 1831 Faraday discovered that an electric current is induced in a wire by moving it in a magnetic field, so as to cut magnetic lines of force. The wire in which the current is induced is an inductor; ignorantly called a conductor.

fastener. An attachment to secure a conductor to a structure.

fathom. A measure of length equal to six feet, used chiefly in taking soundings, measuring cordage, etc.

fatigue. The tendency for a metal to fracture in a brittle manner under conditions of repeated cyclic stressing at stress levels below its tensile strength.

fatigued. A term applied to material, as iron, when it has lost, in some degree, its power of resistance to fracture, due to repeated application of forces, more particularly when the forces or strains have varied greatly in amount.

fatigue of magnetic iron or steel. The change of magnetic hysteresis loss with time. Aging of magnetic material.

fault. An electrical defect.

fault resistance. That resistance which is due to a fault.

84

faure plate. A form of storage battery plate having the active material attached by some mechanical means to the grid proper.

feather. A key with parallel sides sunk into a recess on a shaft or spindle.

feedback. The transfer of electric energy from the output circuit of a device back to its input.

feeder. All circuit conductors between the service equipment or the source of a separately derived system and the final branch circuit overcurrent device.

ferranti cable. A type of electrical conductor designed to carry high tension currents consisting of concentric tubes of copper separated by an insulation of paper saturated with black mineral wax.

ferromagnet. A term sometimes applied to a substance which, like iron, is attracted to a magnet; a substance having paramagnetic properties.

ferromagnetic substance. A substance that has a permeability considerably greater than that of air; a ferromagnetic substance has a permeability that changes with the value of applied magnetizing force.

ferrous. Relating to, or containing iron. An example of non-ferrous would be brass or copper.

festoon lighting. Festoon lighting is a string of outdoor lights suspended between two points more than 15 feet apart.

fiber optics. Piping light is the science that deals with the transmission of light through extremely thin fibers of glass, plastic, or other transparent material.

fibre. One of the delicate, thread like or string like portions of which the tissues of plants and animals are in part constituted; as, the fibre or flax or of muscle.

fibre conduit. This form of conduit consists of pipes made of wood pulp impregnated with a bituminous preservative and insulating compound.

field. A term applied to the space occupied by electric or magnetic lines of force. Also called magnetic field.

field coils. The coils of insulated wire wound upon the field magnets of a dynamo or other rotating machine.

field excitation. The production of an electromagnetic field in a dynamo or motor by supplying a current for magnetizing the field magnets.

field magnet coils. The coils of insulated wire employed to excite the field magnets of a dynamo or motor; the field coils.

field winding. The coil used to provide the magnetizing force in motors and generators.

figure of eight wire. A form of trolley wire having a cross section resembling the shape of the numeral 8.

filament. A wire or ribbon of conducting (resistive) material which develops light and heat energy due to electric charge flow; light radiation is also accompanied by electron emission.

filament of incandescent lamp. The thin wire of infusible conducting material within the bulb of an incandescent lamp. Tungsten is generally used for filaments.

fire stop. Incombustible filler material used to block interior draft spaces.

fish joint. A splice consisting of one or more pieces of iron or wood, bolted to the side or sides of two adjacent rails, where the head of one meets the foot of the other; a fish plate.

fish paper. A superior sheet fibre insulation for armature windings, etc.

fish plate. The plates used with bolts to connect the track rails on railroads.

fish plug. A threaded plug which is screwed into the end of flexible steel conduit and having an eye for attaching a pull wire in drawing the conduit under floors, in partitions, or other difficult places in house wiring.

fish tape. A tempered steel wire, usually of rectangular cross section, that is pushed through a run of conduit and used for pulling the wires through the conduit.

fished wires. In house wiring, wires that have been drawn through ducts, partitions, etc., by the process of fishing.

fishing. A method of running wires through raceways, walls, partitions, etc., by means of a snake; a fish tape.

fishing box. A term at times applied to a junction box.

fission. Fission is a nuclear reaction when the neutron splits a nucleus in two. As it splits, the nucleus throws off extra neutrons. Vast amounts of energy are given off when the nucleus changes.

fitting. An accessory such as a locknut, bushing, or other part of a wiring system that is intended primarily to perform a mechanical rather than an electrical function.

fitting, threadless. A fitting intended for use with electrical metallic tubing or unthreaded rigid conduit.

fixed equipment. A device intended to be permanently connected electrically.

fixed resistance. A nonvariable resistance.

fixture head. An assembly that includes a lamp enclosure or lamp compartment and any components and parts necessary for connecting the lamp compartment to the adapter.

fixture pendant. A fixture that is supported by and suspended from an outlet box by a chain, cord, stem, or cable.

fixture stud. A fitting for mounting a lighting fixture in an outlet box, and which is secured to the box.

fixture wiring. Chain fixtures must be wired with flexible cord, preferably single conductors laced through each link of the fixture chain.

flake of cable. One loop of a horizontally coiled cable.

flame-retardant. So contructed or treated that it will not support or convey flame.

flammable vapors. The vapors given off from a flammable liquid at and above its flash point.

flashing over. In dynamos furnishing high voltage current, the drawing out of a long blue spark from brush to brush on the commutator, when the resistance of the circuit is suddenly changed.

flashover. A disruptive discharge through air, around or over the surface of solid or liquid insulation, between parts of different potential or polarity, produced by the application voltage wherein the breakdown path becomes sufficiently ionized to maintain an electric arc.

flash point. The minimum temperature at which a liquid will give off vapor in sufficient amount to form a flammable air-vapor mixture that can be ignited under specified conditions.

flat cable. A cable made up of conductors laid side by side to permit resting closely against a wall or ceiling.

flatiron, automatic. A flatiron having some form of automatic temperature control, usually a thermostatic control, that operates automatically within predetermined temperature limits to open and close the circuit through the heating element.

fleeting knife. A device on a cable laying machine for guiding the cable over the drum.

flexible conduit system. An underground conduit system constructed in such a manner as to permit the introduction of wires at any time.

flexible lamp cord. A cord composed of insulated flexible conductors, twisted together.

flexible lead. Any electrical conductor that is so stranded as to be readily bent.

flexible metal conduit. A flexible raceway of circular cross section specially constructed for the purpose of the pulling in or the withdrawing of wires or cables after the conduit and its fittings are in place.

floating coil. In a variable ratio transformer voltage regulator, part of the secondary winding which is insulated from the main portion of the winding, and is subdivided by taps into a number of equal sections. The subdivisions of the main secondary winding are much larger, each one being equivalent to the whole of the floating coil.

floating neutral. One whose voltage to ground is free to vary when circuit conditions change.

float switch. A switch in which actuation of the contacts is effected when a float reaches a predetermined level.

float valve. An automatic valve in which the admission of water into a tank or vessel is controlled by a lever attached to a hollow sphere, which floats on the surface and opens or closes the valve, according to its position, as determined by the level of the water.

floodlight. A lighting unit that produces an intensely bright and broad light beam.

floodlighting. The illumination of surfaces, such as building facades, sign boards, etc., to a desired level of illumination intensity.

floor bushing. A bushing intended primarily to be operated entirely indoors in a substantially vertical position to carry a circuit through a floor or horizontal grounded barrier.

floor chisel. In wiring, a wide rod chisel used by electricians for cutting through floors. It is usually 18 to 24 inches long, and must not be used for prying up boards; the ripping chisel is used for that purpose.

floss silk. A soft, smooth, loosely twisted filament silk.

fluorescence. That property by virtue of which certain solids and fluids become luminous under the influence of radiant energy.

fluorescent light. A method of lighting which makes use of ultraviolet energy to activate a fluorescent material coated inside of the bulb's surface. The kind of coating material used depends upon the color effect desired and may consist of zinc silicate, cadmium silicate, or calcium tungsten. These organic materials are known as phosphors, which powder transforms short-wave invisible radiation into visible light.

fluorescent-mercury lamp. An electric-discharge lamp having a high-pressure mercury arc in an arc tube, and an outer envelope coated with a fluorescent substance (phosphor) that transforms some of the ultraviolet energy generated by the arc into light.

flush switch. A switch so placed as to be flush with the surface of the wall or woodwork on which it is mounted.

flux. In soldering or brazing, a substance applied to the portions to be united, causing the solder to flow easily and adhere to the joint.

90

flux field. All electric or magnetic lines of force in a given region.

flywheel alternator. A revolving field alternator of very large size in which the field magnets are mounted on a casting having a central hub and spokes, the assembly resembling a flywheel.

fog, electric. A fog which sometimes arises when the atmosphere contains an unusual amount of free electricity.

foil. A thin metal conductor intended to be bonded to a protected surface so that the conductor will break when the protected surface is cut or broken.

foiled conductor. A conductor having an outside coating of tin foil.

footcandle. A unit of illumination; the degree of illumination produced by a lumin-luminous flux of one lumen per square foot of surface area.

footing. Structural unit used to distribute loads to the bearing materials.

foot lambert. In illumination, a unit of brightness; one lumen emitted or reflected per square foot of surface.

footlight. A striplight located at foot level along the front of the stage or cyclorama (a stretched cloth across the back of the stage used to form the background).

foot pound. A unit of work. It is the work done when a weight of one pound is raised to the height of one foot.

foot switch. A switch that is suitable for operation by an operator's foot.

foot valve. The lowermost valve in a pump through which the fluid is drawn into the working barrel or pump chamber.

force. An elementary physical cause capable of modifying the motion of a mass.

forked lightning. A form of lightning discharge which seems to split into branches or to follow a zigzag path; zigzag lightning.

formula. A prescribed form, principle, or rule expressed in mathematical terms, chemical symbols, etc.

formulae. A rule or principle expressed in algebraic language.

foucault currents. A term expressive of eddy currents, particularly when in armature cores. Useless currents created in a conducting mass by the movement through magnetic flux.

four pole switch. A type of switch designed to control four circuits. Note that the number of points (referring to a single pole switch) is equal to the number of live contacts, not including the pivot contact. That is, one less than the number of external wires.

four-way switch. One used in a circuit that permits a single lamp to be controlled from any of three or more positions: It has four terminals which alternately are joined together in different pairs.

fraction. A quantity less than a unit or whole number. Fractions take their name and value from the number of parts into which the unit is divided. Thus, if the unit is divided into two equal parts, one of these parts is called one-half.

frame size. A term applied to a group of circuit breakers of similar physical configuration. Frame size is expressed in amperes and corresponds to the largest ampere rating available in the group. The same frame size designation may be applied to more than one group of circuit breakers.

Franklin, Benjamin. Born 1706, died 1790. An American scientist, philosopher, and statesman. He demonstrated the identity of lightning with electricity by his famous kite experiment in 1752, and as a result invented the lightning rod.

free electricity. The ordinary start of electricity upon a charged conductor, not in the presence of a charge of the opposite kind. A free charge will flow away to the earth if a conducting path is provided.

free electrons. Electrons which are loosely held consequently tend to move at random among the atoms of the material.

freezing point. The point at which a liquid tends to become a solid by loss of heat. The freezing point of water is 32 degrees F when the barometer reads 29.921 ins.

frequency. The number of periods occurring in unit time of a periodic process, such as in the flow of electric charge. The number of complete cycles per second existing in any form of wave motion; such as the number of cycles per second of an alternating current.

frequency changing set. A combination of a synchronous motor and an alternator wound to give a desired change in frequency. Sometimes called frequency converter but preferably frequency changer.

friction. The effect of rubbing. The resistance which a moving body meets with by the contact of another body.

friction tape. A fibrous tape impregnated with a sticky moisture-resistant compound that provides a protective covering for insulation.

frictional torque. The torque in a motor which is required to be exerted on the armature in order to neutralize the friction. Torque is produced by friction.

front of machine. Usually the end of the machine at which the commutator or collector rings are found.

frost line. Deepest level below grade to which frost penetrates in a geographic area.

full arc. A term sometimes applied to an arc lamp of 2,000 nominal candlepower.

Fullerboard. A fibrous material much harder than paper. It is flexible, durable, and is largely used in insulating the coils of electric machines; also known as presspahn.

full-load amps. The amount of current, in amps, in an electrical circuit when the load is operating in a full-capacity condition.

fulminate. A term applied to explosives of high explosive properties.

furring strips. Wooden strips attached to a cinder block wall to allow for the depth of an outlet box.

fuse. A strip of wire or metal inserted in series with a circuit which, when it carries an excess of current over its rated capacity, will burn out. Also called a cutout.

fuse alloy. An alloy of lead with a small percentage of tin, used for electric safety fuses because it readily melts under the heat of an electric current when the current becomes too strong for the safety of the circuit.

fuse block. A block of porcelain or other insulating material upon which one or more safety fuses are mounted.

fuse characteristics. The operation of fuses differs from plain overload circuit breakers in that they are governed by both time and quantity of the current.

fuse clips. The contacts on a base, fuse support, or fuse mounting, for connecting into the circuit. The current responsive element with its holding means, if such means are used for making a complete device.

fuse, current-limiting. A fuse that properly interrupts all available currents within its interrupting rating and, within its current-limiting range, limits the clearing time at rated voltage to an interval equal to or less than the first major or symmetrical current loop duration and limits peak let-through current to a value less than the peak current that would be possible with the fuse replaced by a solid conductor of the same impedance.

fuse cutout. An assembly consisting of a fuse support and holder, which may also include a fuse link.

fuse element. Also termed "fuse link"; the current-carrying part of a fuse that opens the circuit when subjected to excessive current.

fuse holder. A supporting device for a fuse that provides terminal connections.

fuse hook. A hook provided with an insulating handle for opening and closing fuses or switches and for inserting the fuseholder, fuse unit, or disconnecting blade into and removing it from the fuse support.

fuse links. Links of fusible material designed for safety fuses.

fuse tongs. Tongs provided with an insulating handle and jaws. Fuse tongs are used to insert the fuseholder or fuse unit into the fuse support or to remove it from the support.

fusing current. The current required to melt a safety fuse.

fusion. Fusion is a nuclear reaction. Fusion is the joining of hydrogen atoms which causes heat hotter than the sun.

G

gain. The ratio of the output power, voltage, or current to the input power, voltage, or current, respectively.

Galvanic cell. A cell in which chemical change is the source of electric energy. It usually consists of two dissimilar conductors in contact with each other and with an electrolyte, or two similar conductors in contact with each other and with dissimilar electrolytes.

Galvanic current. In electrotherapy, a smooth or even current obtained from a copper oxide rectifier which changes the AC to DC.

Galvanic multiplier. A name formerly given to the galvanometer.

galvanizing. The process of coating metals with zinc to prevent corrosion.

galvanometer. A current indicator. It consists of a magnetic needle suspended within a coil of wire and free to swing over the face of a graduated dial. The movement of the needle shows the direction of the current and indicates whether it is a strong or weak one. There are numerous types of galvanometers such as; astatic, tangent, sine, differential, ballistic, and D'Arsonval.

gang switch. Two or more rotary switches on one shaft and operated by the same control.

gang switch box. A box containing an assembly of switches.

gangway cable. A cable designed to be installed horizontally (or nearly so) for power circuits in mine gangways and entries.

gap, spark. A high-voltage device with electrodes between which a disruptive discharge of electricity may pass, usually through air.

garage. A building or portion of a building in which one or more self-propelled vehicles carrying volatile flammable liquid for fuel or power are kept for use, sale, storage, rental, repair, exhibition, or demonstrating purposes, and all that portion of a building which is on or below the floor or floors in which such vehicles are kept and which is not separated therefrom by suitable cutoffs.

gas. That fluid form of matter which is elastic and tends to expand indefinitely.

gaseous discharge. The emission of light from gas atoms excited by an electric current.

gas-filled cable. A self-contained pressure cable in which the pressure medium is an inert gas having access to the insulation.

gasket-sealed relay. A relay in an enclosure sealed with a gasket.

gasproof. So constructed or protected that the specified gas will not interfere with successful operation.

gastight. So constructed that gas or air can neither enter nor leave the structure except through vents or piping provided for that purpose.

gas voltmeter. A device for measuring the strength of an electric current by determining the volume of gas involved by the electrolysis, which the current produces in a solution through which it is caused to pass.

gate. A device or element that, depending upon one or more specified inputs, has the ability to permit or inhibit the passage of a signal.

gate valve. A type of valve having two inclined seats between which the valve wedges down in closing, the passage through the valve being in an uninterrupted line from one end to the other, while the valve, when opened, is drawn up into a dome or recess, thus leaving a straight passage the full diameter of the pipe.

97

gauge. A measure; a standard of measurement; an instrument to determine dimensions or capacity.

gauss. The unit of a magnetic field strength. It is the intensity of field which acts on a unit pole with a force of one dyne. It is equal to one line of force per square centimeter or 6.45 lines per sq. in. of cross section.

gaussmeter. A magnetometer provided with a scale graduated in gauss or kilogauss.

gear. A word used collectively for an assembly of parts as toothed wheels, chain and sprockets, links, etc., used to transmit motion.

geissler tubes. Sealed tubes of glass containing highly rarefied gases, either with or without fluorescent liquids or solids or both, and provided with platinum electrodes passing through and fused into the glass; luminous effects being produced on the passage of the electric discharges.

general lighting. Lighting designed to provide a substantially uniform level of illumination throughout an area, exclusive of any provision for special local requirements.

general-purpose branch circuit. A branch circuit that supplies a number of outlets for lighting and appliances.

general purpose motor. Any motor of 200 or less horsepower and 450 or more r.p.m. having a continuous time rating, and designed, listed, or offered in standard ratings for use without restriction to a particular application.

general-use snap switch. A form of general-use switch so constructed that it can be installed in flush device boxes, or on outlet box covers, or otherwise used in conjunction with wiring systems recognized by the Code.

generated voltage. A voltage produced in a closed path or circuit by the relative motion of the circuit or its parts with respect to magnetic flux.

generator. A general name given to a machine for transforming mechanical energy into electrical energy.

geodesic. The shortest line between two points measured on any mathematically derived surface, that includes the points.

geometry. That branch of pure mathematics that treats of space and its relations. In other words, it is the science of the mutual relations of points, lines, angles, surfaces, and solids, considered as having no properties except those arising from extension and difference of situation.

germanium. A metal of gray white color and fine metallic luster. It melts at 1562 degrees F.

german-silver alloy. An alloy composed of 1/2 copper, 1/4 zinc, 1/4 nickel, and used for wires of resistance coils.

giga. A prefix meaning one billion (1,000,000,000), such as gigahertz (GHz).

gilbert. The unit of magnetic pressure. It is equal to the magnetic pressure of .7958 ampere turn.

girder armature. An armature whose core in shape resembles a girder or H.

gland seal. A seal used to prevent leakage between a moveable and a fixed part.

glare. The sensation produced by brightnesses within the visual field that are sufficiently greater than the luminance to which the eyes are adapted to cause annoyance, discomfort, or loss in visual performance and visibility.

glass. A hard, brittle, usually transparent substance made by melting together sand or silica with lime, potash, soda, or lead oxide.

glass fuse. A fuse enclosed within a glass tube.

glass insulator. A line wire insulator which is cheaper than porcelain, and owing to its transparency can be more easily examined, but glass is less strong both mechanically and electrically, and more apt to collect a film of moisture, and so for high tension transmission, porcelain is almost exclusively employed.

glaze. A gloss or smooth transparent surface applied to porcelain, as in the manufacture of insulators for high tension circuits. It is generally composed of an admixture of alkalies with silica, lime, and often oxide or carbonate of lead.

globe. A transparent or diffusing enclosure intended to protect a lamp, to diffuse and redirect its light, or to change the color of the light.

globe strain insulator. A form of insulator employed in strain, or pullover wires in a trolley line, consisting of a pair of interlocking rings which are kept insulated from each other by means of an insulating ball or globe in which they are embedded; a spherical strain insulator.

gloves. In electric repair work special rubber gloves are used to prevent the frequent and often fatal accidents occurring to linemen from shock while handling electric light wires or other wires in contact with the same. Gloves are also useful in handling the acids of batteries.

glow coil. A coil caused to become red hot by electrical current flowing through it to light the pilot burner gas on automatic-pilot ignition systems.

glow discharge. A variety of convective discharge seen at the tip of a pointed conductor.

glower. In the Nernst lamp, the pencil of refractory oxides which becomes incandescent upon the passage of the electric current.

glow factor. A measure of the visible light response of a fluorescent material to black light.

glow lamp. An electric discharge lamp whose mode of operation is that of a glow discharge and in which light is generated in the space close to the electrodes.

glucinum. A rare metallic element of a white color, resembling magnesium in its properties.

gold. A conductor of electricity, noted for its beautiful yellow color, ductility, malleability, and freedom from liability to rust or tarnish. Its specific gravity is 19.3 and melting point 2000 degrees F.

gold bath. An electrolyzable solution of gold salt used for depositing the metal in the electroplating process; a gold plate, which acts as the anode, being immersed in the liquid opposite the article to be plated, and which article acts as the cathode.

governor. A device or attachment for controlling and regulating the speed of a prime mover, usually by means of centrifugal force.

grab load. In crane loading, a load of from 1 to 1 1/2 tons.

gradient. At a point, a vector equal to, and in the direction of, the maximum space rate of change of the field.

gradient, electric. The rate of increase or decrease of a variable magnitude, sometimes used for the curve that represents a variable current.

gradometer. A variety of clinometer, consisting of a curved glass vial filled with alcohol and a graduated scale. The position of the bubble shows the degree of the gradient.

graduated. Marked to indicate a number of operating positions.

gramme. A unit of weight equivalent to the weight of one cubic centimeter of pure water at its maximum density at a temperature of 39.2 degress F, in a vacuum.

gramme colorie. The quantity of heat which is necessary to raise a gramme of water one degree centigrade.

gramaphone. An instrument which records and reproduces articulate speech.

graphic method. The system or method of solving problems in the equalization or distribution of forces, stresses, loads, etc., by means of accurately drawn figures and diagrams.

graphic symbol. A geometric representation used to depict graphically the generic function of an item as it normally is used in a circuit.

graphite. A condition of carbon distinguished by its softness and metallic luster, and serving to write on paper and other suitable material surfaces.

graphite brush. A brush composed principally of graphite.

graphite coating. A layer of powdered graphite sometimes distributed over an insulating surface in order to render the surface a good conductor of electricity, especially in electrotyping when a mold requires a surface of metal for printing purposes.

grappling. Recovering a sunken cable or other object with a grapnel.

grapnel. An implement having flukes of prongs for grappling purposes; a grappling iron for seizing a submarine cable or other object underwater.

gravity. A force which gives to every particle of matter a tendency toward every other particle. This influence is conveyed from one body to another without any perceptible interval of time. The weight of the body is the force it exerts in consequence of its gravity, and is measured by its mechanical effects.

gray iron. A quality of iron which is softer and less brittle than white iron. It is, to a slight degree, malleable and flexible and can be easily drilled and turned in a lathe, and does not resist the file.

greatest common divisor. The greatest number that will exactly divide each of two or more numbers.

green candle. A standard candle having a green glass screen for the purpose of measuring the candlepower of an arc lamp.

grid. A lead plate for a storage cell; it is provided with corrugations or perforations so that it may be capable of holding a large amount of the active material, and thus increase the capacity of the cell.

grille. A perforated or louvered covering for an air passage, usually installed in a sidewall, ceiling, or floor.

grip of belt. The hold which a driving belt has upon the pulley.

ground. A conducting connection, whether intentional or accidental, between an electrical circuit or equipment and the earth, or to some conducting body that serves in place of the earth.

ground bus. A bus to which the grounds from individual pieces of equipment are connected, and that in turn, is connected to ground at one or more points.

ground clamp. A clamp used in connecting a grounding conductor to a grounding electrode or to a thing grounded.

ground detector. An instrument used for detecting (and sometimes measuring) the leakage to earth or the insulation of a line or network and is sometimes called ground or earth indicator, or leakage detector.

grounded. Connected to earth or to some conducting body that serves in place of the earth.

grounded circuit. A circuit in which one conductor or point (usually the neutral conductor or neutral point of transformer or generator windings) is intentionally grounded, either solidly or through a grounding device.

grounded conductor. A system or circuit conductor that is intentionally grounded.

grounded, effectively. An expression that means grounded through a grounding connection of sufficiently low impedance that fault grounds that may occur cannot build up voltages in excess of limits established for circuits, apparatus, or systems so grounded.

grounded neutral system. A system in which the neutral is connected to ground, either solidly or through a resistance or reactance of low value.

grounded, solidly. Grounded through an adequate ground connection in which no impedance has been inserted intentionally.

grounded system. A system of conductors in which at least one conductor or point (usually the middle conductor or neutral) is intentionally grounded.

ground fault. Denotes an unintentional electrical path between a part operating normally at some potential to ground, and ground.

ground-fault circuit interrupter (GFCI). A device intended for protection of personnel that functions to de-energize a circuit or portion thereof, within an established period of time, when a current to ground exceeds some predetermined value that is less than that required to operate the overcurrent protective device of the supply equipment.

ground-fault circuit interrupter (GFCI) tester. A device with no receptacle outlet that, when plugged into a receptacle and activated, circulates current through the ungrounded circuit conductor and the grounding conductor, and then indicates by a pattern of lights, or other similar means, whether a GFCI connected to the branch circuit is functioning.

ground-fault protection of equipment. A system intended to provide protection of equipment from damaging line-to-ground fault currents by operating to cause a disconnecting means to open all ungrounded conductors of the faulted circuit. This protection is provided at current levels less than those required to protect conductors from damage through the operation of a supply circuit overcurrent device.

ground-fault relaying equipment. That element of ground-fault current sensing and relaying equipment, that responds to a specified signal from a ground-fault sensor. The output of such relaying equipment may (1) include a switching device, (2) transmit a trip energy signal, or (3) by a combination of (1) and (2) that is directly or indirectly capable of causing a disconnecting device to operate. The power to operate the relaying equipment may be derived from the ground fault, from a separate source, or both.

ground-fault sensor. That element of ground-fault sensing and relaying equipment that detects ground-fault current and transmits a resulting signal to ground-fault relaying equipment.

ground grid. A system of grounding electrodes, consisting of interconnected bare cables buried in the earth, to provide a common ground for electric devices and metallic structures.

grounding. In wiring, the intentional connection of a circuit to the earth for the purpose of insuring safety from shock. Thus, if any live conductor is efficiently connected to earth, a person touching the conductor cannot receive a shock, since there is no difference of pressure between the earth on which he is standing and the conductor which he is touching. When a circuit is intentionally grounded, the voltage of the grounded point is made permanently that of the earth and the voltage of every other point of the circuit becomes fixed with respect to ground. When one conductor is grounded it depends upon which conductor a person touches as to whether he receives a shock.

grounding conductor. A conductor used to connect equipment or the grounded circuit of a wiring system to a grounding electrode or electrodes.

grounding conductor, equipment. The conductor used to connect the noncurrent-carrying metal parts of equipment, raceways, and other enclosures to the system grounded conductor and/or the grounding electrode conductor at the service equipment or at the source of a separately derived system.

grounding electrode conductor. The conductor used to connect the grounding electrode to the equipment grounding conductor and/or to the grounded conductor of the circuit at the service equipment or at the source of a separately derived system.

grounding jumper, appliances. A strap or wire to connect the frame of the range to the neutral conductor of the supply circuit.

grounding point, patient. A jack or terminal bus that serves as the collection point for redundant grounding of electric appliances serving a patient vicinity, and for grounding conductive furniture or nonelectric equipment within reach of a patient or a person who may touch him.

grounding, protective. A system for connecting noncurrent carrying conductive parts of the equipment to ground.

grounding outlet. An outlet equipped with a receptacle of the polarity type having, in addition to the current-carrying contacts, one grounded contact that can be used for the connection of an equipment grounding conductor.

grounding terminal. A designated terminal screw or pressure wire connector located on the internal wall of the field wiring compartment for connection to an equipment grounding conductor from the panelboard.

ground lug. A lug used in connecting a grounding conductor to a grounding electrode or to equipment grounded.

ground relay. A relay that by its design or application is intended to respond primarily to system ground faults.

ground rod. A rod that is driven into the ground to serve as a ground terminal, such as a copper-clad rod, solid copper rod, galvanized iron rod, or galvanized iron pipe.

grouping of phrases. The method of connecting the separate windings on an AC machine. In polyphase alternators, the separate windings of the various phases may be grouped either delta or wye.

grout. A very rich concrete used to bond the feet, sole plates, bedplate, or rail of a machine to its foundation.

grouting. In construction work, the pouring of a mixture of cement, sand, and water into the voids of stone, brick or concrete work, either to give a solid bearing or to fasten anchor bolts, dowels, etc.

growler. An audible electric testing device for armatures. In operation, the AC which is used, sets up vibrations at the contact surfaces between armature core and growler poles resulting in a buzzing or growling noise. Every armature, no matter if it be good or bad, when placed on a growler with current turned on will growl, and this noise is no indication as to the condition of the armature.

107

guard. A part or an assembly provided for shielding an area that would otherwise introduce a risk of fire, electric shock, or injury to persons.

guard arm. In pole line construction, an upright attached to a cross arm to prevent a wire falling, in case it becomes detached from its insulator.

guarded. Covered, shielded, fenced, enclosed, or otherwise protected by means of suitable covers, casings, barriers, rails, screens, mats, or platforms to remove the likelihood of approach or contact by persons or objects to a point of danger.

guard rail. A barrier secured to uprights and erected along the exposed or open side and ends of a platform.

guard wire. A wire stretched parallel with a trolley wire and just above it to prevent other wires falling across and making electrical contact with the live wire; a running guard wire.

gutta percha. A substance obtained from the gum of a tropical tree found in the East Indies. It has many of the properties of India rubber and is of great value in electrical work for its insulating powers and durability.

gutter, auxiliary. A section of wireway used to supplement the wiring space at a distribution center, switchboard, or similar location in a wiring system.

gutter of insulator. A depression in an insulator to lead off rain water.

guy. A rod, wire, or other appliance for stiffening a pole, or for steadying a system of overhead wires.

guy anchor. The buried element of a guy assembly that provides holding strength or resistance to guy wire pull.

guy for poles. A brace consisting of heavy galvanized wires to take any lateral stress to which a pole may be subjected. The guys are attached near the top and secured either to the base of the next pole, to a suitable guy stub or post, or to a guy anchor, which is buried about eight feet in the earth and held down by stones and concrete.

guy wire. A stranded cable used for a semiflexible tension support between a pole or structure and the anchor rod, or between structures.

gyration. The act of turning or whirling around a fixed center.

gyrostat. A fly wheel whose revolving motion is gyrostatic.

H

halation. In illumination, the halo effect seen around light sources which causes the outlines of the letters in a sign to appear blurred.

half coil winding. An armature winding in which the coils in any phase are situated opposite every other pole, that is, a winding in which there is only one coil per phase per pair of poles. Also called hemitropie winding.

half hoof magnet. A semicircular magnet.

hand hole. An opening large enough to readily admit the hand, provided in an underground conduit for the purpose of gaining access to the cable.

hand rule. Generally known as Fleming's hand rule.

hanger. A unit assembly used singly or in combination with other assemblies for supporting or hanging pipe.

hard drawn wire. Wire as it comes from the drawing machines without tempering.

hard rubber. A name often given to vulcanite or ebonite which is India rubber "vulcanized" by a large admixture of sulphur. It is often used in the manufacture of electrical instruments.

hard solder. A fusible alloy, ordinarily composed of copper and zinc, or copper, zinc, and silver.

hard-start kit. A group of components used to increase the starting torque of an electric motor. It consists of a starting capacitor, a relay, and the necessary wiring to install the kit on the unit.

hard steel. A loose and indefinite term, meaning all steel that is not mild, it may be taken as steel containing over 1/2 of 1 percent of carbon.

hardware. Parts made of metal such as fasteners, hinges, etc.

harmonic. A sinusoidal component of a periodic wave or quantity having a frequency that is an integral multiple of the fundamental frequency. A component, the frequency of which is twice the fundamental frequency, is called the second harmonic.

harmonics. Ocillations to which a circuit will respond, of which the frequency is an odd or even multiple of the fundamental frequency. Harmonics are usually objectionable; the power that goes into them is wasted.

haulage, electric. The moving of car or vessel by the action of electricity.

hazardous location. An area where ignitible vapors or dust may cause a fire or explosion created by energy emitted from lighting or other electric equipment or by electrostatic generation.

header. A transverse raceway for electric conductors, providing access to predetermined cells of a cellular metal floor, thereby permitting the installation of electric conductors from a distribution center to the cells.

head guy. A guy made fast to the top of a pole.

heat. That form of energy which consists in the agitation of the molecules of matter by which heat is produced; the state of a substance in which it produces the sensation of heat. Heat is distinguished as sensible and latent.

heat coil. A protective device that grounds or opens a circuit, or does both, by means of a mechanical element that is allowed to move when the fusible substance that holds it in place is heated above a predetermined temperature by current in the circuit.

heat, electric. The heat produced in a conductor by the passage of an electric current through it.

heater. A term sometimes used for the thermal running overload protective device in a motor circuit.

heating anticipator. A resistor located inside the thermostat and placed in series with the temperature-control circuit during the heating cycle to cause a false heat inside the thermostat. This causes the thermostat to stop the heating equipment before the temperature inside the space actually reaches the set point.

heating by electricity. The method of obtaining heat by passing an electric current through a high resistance conductor called a resistance wire or heating unit. The heat thus produced is used for various domestic and industrial purposes.

heating cycle. One complete operation of the thermostat from ON to ON or from OFF to OFF.

heating effect of the current. A conductor along which a current flows becomes heated. The rise of temperature may be small or great according to circumstances, but some heat is always produced. The heat effect is manifested in different degrees in different metals, according to their varying conducting powers. The poorest conductors, such as platinum and iron, suffer much greater changes of temperature by the same charge than the best conductors, such as gold and copper. The charge of electricity which only elevates the temperature of one conductor a small amount, will sometimes render another incandescent, and vaporize a third.

heating element. A length of resistance metal in the form of a strip, or coiled wire through which electric current is passed to give off heat. It becomes hot on account of the resistance it offers to the current. Also called heating unit.

heat lightning. Lightning visible in broad flashes near the horizon and unaccompanied by thunder, observed when a storm is at a great distance.

heat loss. The part of the transmission loss due to the conversion of electric energy into heat.

heat loss from buildings. Heat escapes from buildings two ways: (1) by conduction through the windows, walls, roof, and floor, and (2) by leakage of warm air. The loss is proportional to the difference in temperature between the inside and outside air.

heat pump. An electrically operated device designed to extract heat from one location and transfer this heat to another location. A heat pump is used for both heating and cooling and reverses the refrigeration cycle when heating is needed. The condenser provides the heat while the evaporator is arranged to pick up heat from air, water, etc. By shifting the flow of refrigerant, the heat pump system is used to cool the space.

heat sink. A part used to absorb heat.

heat treating. Heating and cooling a solid metal or alloy in such a way as to obtain desired conditions or properties, commonly used as a shop term to denote a thermal treatment to increase strength.

heavy water. Used in nuclear energy. It is a clear, colorless liquid that looks and tastes like ordinary tap water. It occurs naturally in water in minute quantities; about one part heavy water to 7,000 parts ordinary water. Roughly 340,000 tons of lake water are needed to produce one ton of heavy water. Heavy water is about 30 times better than ordinary water in slowing down the neutrons without absorbing them.

hekto. A prefix for one hundred.

helical coil. A coil of wire elongated like the turns of a screw; a helix.

helical spring. A spring whose coils have a gradually decreasing diameter, either lying flat in one plane like a watch spring, or assuming a conical form. The helical spring coiled on a cylinder is generally known as a spiral spring.

hellotropism. A twisting on the growth of stalks and stems resulting from the influence of any light source.

hemlock. A variety of spruce or fir, used largely for telegraph poles, found along the northern border of the United States and in Canada. The wood is rough and splintery.

henry. The practical unit of self-induction, equal to 10 degrees absolute units of induction. It receives its name from Henry, an American scientist. The self-induction of a circuit is one henry when the induced pressure is one volt, while the inducing current varies at the rate of one ampere per second. The henry is, therefore, the coefficient by which the time rate of change of the current in the circuit must be multiplied, in order to give the voltage of self-induction in the circuit.

hermetically sealed. A compressor or other device enclosed in a gastight housing.

hermetic motor. A stator and rotor without shaft, end shields, or bearings for installation in refrigeration compressors of the hermetically sealed type.

hermetic refrigerant motor-compressor. A combination consisting of a compressor and motor, both of which are enclosed in the same housing, with no external shaft or shaft seals; the motor operating in the refrigerant.

hertz (hz). The frequency in cycles per second of an AC power source. In the United States this power is generally 60 hertz. One hertz = one cycle per second.

hickey (conduit bender). A form of hand conduit bender consisting of a long lever having at one end a slot at right angles, which fits over and grips the conduit when pressure is brought on the lever or handle to bend the conduit.

hickey (fitting). A fitting used to mount a lighting fixture in an outlet box or on a pipe or stud. It has openings through which fixture wires may be brought out of the fixture stem.

high commutator bars. Commutator bars which in the normal wear of the commutator project beyond the others and require turning down to restore cylindrical symmetry.

high-impedance rotor. An induction-motor rotor having a high impedance squirrel cage, used to limit starting current.

high-leg, delta. Generally the center phase. It's to be colored orange or tagged. The high-leg voltage to neutral on a 230/115v system would be 199 volts.

high mica. This condition occurs after some wear if the mica is too hard or brushes too soft and results in heating and burning of the commutator bars due to arcing. In severe cases the solder melts, resulting in open circuits due to leads becoming disconnected. To remedy this condition the mica must be undercut. Often called "slotting" the commutator.

high-potential test (high-pot). A test that consists of the application of a voltage higher than the rated voltage for a specified time for the purpose of determining the adequacy against breakdown of insulating materials and spacings under normal conditions.

high-pressure control. A control designed to sense the discharge pressure of a compressor and to stop the compressor when this pressure reaches an unsafe point to prevent damage to the compressor motor.

high-reactance rotor. A induction-motor rotor having a high reactance squirrel cage, used where low starting current is required and where low locked-rotor and breakdown torques are acceptable.

high-resistance connectors. Connecting wires of high resistance between the armature winding and the commutator bars. Used to prevent sparking at the brushes.

high slip motor. An induction motor having high armature resistance. This type, up to a certain point, will have increased starting torque without change in maximum or pull out torque.

high tension current. A high voltage current. The word high tension refers to pressure of 1000 or more volts.

hinge clip. The clip to which the blade is movably attached on a switching device.

hinge jaw. The jaw of a switch to which the blade is pivoted.

hitching up. "Hitching up" is an expression used for inserting a "booster" into an electric system.

hoist. An apparatus for moving a load by the application of a pulling force, and not including a car or platform running in guides.

hoist, electric. A hoist operated by an electric motor, the power being applied to the hoisting drum through a suitable transmission.

hoistway. Any shaftway, hatchway, well hole, or other vertical opening or space in which an elevator or dumbwaiter is designed to operate.

homopolar dynamo. A dynamo in which a conductor moves continuously around one pole of a magnet; a unipolar dynamo, of which Faraday's disc is a type.

hook stick. A device with an insulated handle and hook or other means for performing stick operation of a switching device.

horn. A tube of varying cross-sectional area for radiating or receiving acoustic waves.

horology, electric. The application of electricity to the regulation and control of the movement of clocks.

horsepower (hp). Unit used to express rate of work, or power. One horsepower = 746 watts. Work done at the rate of 33,000 foot pounds per minute or 550 foot pounds per second.

horseshoe magnet. A magnet bent into the shape of a horseshoe or the letter U, thereby bringing the two poles together so that they act at the same time upon the armature or keeper.

hot. An appliance, fitted with heating elements and arranged to support a flat-bottom utensil containing the material to be heated.

hot plate. An appliance, fitted with heating elements and arranged to support a flat-bottom utensil containing the material to be heated.

hottest spot temperature allowance. A conventional value selected to approximate the degrees of temperature by which the limiting insulation temperature rise exceeds the limiting observable temperature rise.

hot wire. The ungrounded wire in a circuit.

hot-wire relay. A relay that is designed to help start a split-phase compressor motor by directing the electric current to the start winding. The relay removes the start winding from the circuit by causing a bimetal switch to warp open because of the current flowing through the relay.

household equipment. Equipment intended for use around or in a residence. Portable, cord-connected, insect electrocution equipment intended for use during camping, or the like, is also considered household equipment.

house load. This load is connected to the house meter. It is the lighting and equipment usage the owner is paying for, such as hallway lighting, parking lot lighting, tennis court, pool, laundry, etc.

housing. That section of the device that encloses and is intended to protect operating parts, control mechanisms, or other mechanical or electrical components, the damage of which would render the device incapable of being operated as intended, lead to tampering, introduce the possibility of escape of liquid, or expose bare live electrical parts.

howler. A particularly noisy variety of electric buzzer.

hue. The attribute of color perception that determines whether it is red, yellow, green, blue, purple, or the like.

hum. A low-pitched droning noise, consisting of several harmonically related frequencies, resulting from an AC power supply.

humidifier. An apparatus to add water vapor to the atmosphere; to add water vapor or moisture to any material.

humidity. The amount of water vapor in the air. This depends on the temperature of the air. When there is mixed with the air, all of the water vapor which it can hold, the air is said to be saturated. The quantity of water vapor actually present in a given volume of air, without regard to its temperature, is called its absolute humidity.

humming of transformer. A sound produced in a transformer core, due to the rapid reversal of the magnetic flux. It may be caused partly by the contraction and expansion of the iron itself, and partly by the mutual attraction and repulsion of any loose core plates.

hunting. The state of two parallel connected alternators running out of step, or not synchronously, that is "see-sawing".

hybrid coil. A single transformer having effectively three windings which, within certain limitations as to the impedances to which it is connected, performs the function of a hybrid set.

hydraulic elevator. A power elevator where the energy is applied by means of a liquid under pressure in a cylinder equipped with a plunger or piston.

hydraulic operation. Power operation by movement of a liquid under pressure.

hydraulics. That branch of the science of engineering which deals with water in motion, and the application of its laws to the industries; as to hydroelectric generation.

hydrocarbon. A compound of hydrogen and carbon; the possible number of these compounds is infinite; and the known number is very large.

hydrochloric acid. A colorless gas with a keen acid smell. It liquifies under pressure of 40 atmospheres at 10 degrees and solidifies at 115 degrees. The gas is very soluble in water and its solution behaves as a strong acid. It is obtained on a large scale by heating common salt with sulphuric acid.

hydrodynamics. That branch of mechanics which deals with the laws of motion and action of water and other liquids.

hydroelectric central station. The economy with which electricity can be transmitted long distance by high tension. AC has led to the development of a large number of water powers in more or less remote regions.

hydroelectric machine. A machine for generating electricity by the friction of jets of steam issuing from an insulated boiler, through wooden nozzles, against a metal comb.

hydrogen. A colorless, odorless, tasteless gas; the lightest body known.

hydrogenerator. A generator driven by a hydraulic turbine or water wheel.

hydrometer. An instrument for measuring the specific gravity of liquids. Often used to check batteries.

hydrostatic bed. In hydraulics, a water bed; as that of a pond.

hygrometer. An instrument for measuring the amount of water vapor in the air.

hypotenuse. The side of a right angled triangle opposite the right angle.

hypothesis. A proposition or principle which is assumed in order to draw an inference or conclusion in proof of the point of question. A theory assumed to account for known phenomena.

hysteresis. The lagging of magnetism, in a magnetic metal, behind the magnetizing flux which produces it. Hysteresis is due to the friction between the molecules of iron or other magnetic substance which requires an expenditure of energy to change their position. The expenditure of energy is converted into heat.

hysteresis in transformer core. In the operation of a transformer the AC causes the core to undergo rapid reversals of magnetism. This requires an expenditure of energy which is converted into heat. The loss of energy is due to the work required to change the position of the molecules of the iron, in reversing the magnetization. Extra power then must be taken from the line to make up for this loss, thus reducing the efficiency of the transformer.

hysteretic lag. Lagging of magnetization caused by hysteresis.

hz. The abbreviation for hertz (cycles).

I

I. Symbol for electric current.

I-beam. A rolled joist or beam resembling the capital letter I in cross section. Such beams are economical of material through elimination of redundant material near the neutral axis.

identified (as applied to equipment). Recognizable as suitable for the specific purpose, function, use, environment, application, etc., where described in a particular Code requirement.

idio electrics. A name formerly given to substances, such as glass, amber, and resin, which become electrified by friction.

idle bar. An open circuited conductor bar in the rotor of a squirrel-cage motor, used to give low starting current in a moderate torque motor.

idle coil. A coil through which no current is passing.

idle current. A name sometimes given to that component of an alternating current at right angles to the voltage and contributing nothing to the power.

idle time. The portion of the available time during which a system is believed to be in good operating condition but is not in productive use.

igniter. A device used in low tension ignition for lighting the charge operating by the sudden breaking of contact between two electrodes to produce an electric arc. A primary induction coil in the circuit gives the necessary inductive effect to prolong the arc sufficiently for ignition.

ignitor-sensor. Flame-safe equipment designed to ignite the pilot-burner gas and then sense if there is a flame present. If no flame is present or if the flame is not satisfactory to ignite the main burner gas, the control system will not open the main gas valve.

121

ignition coil. A primary or secondary coil forming a part of a low tension (make and break) or high tension (jump spark) ignition system respectively.

ignitor. A stationary electrode that is partly immersed in the cathode pool and has the function of initiating a cathode spot.

illumination. The density of light flux projected on a surface; it denotes the art of using artificial sources of light, that is to say, the problem of illumination involves the selection and arrangement of these artificial sources of light so that the objects to be lighted will show up to the best advantage and with the minimum amount of artificial light.

impedance. The total opposition which a circuit offers the flow of alternating current at a given frequency; combination of resistance and reactance, measured in ohms.

impedance factor. The ratio of the impedance to the ohmic resistance in an electric circuit.

impedor. A device, the purpose of which is to introduce impedance into an electric circuit.

impregnate. The act of adding impregnant to insulation or a winding.

impregnation, winding. The process of applying an insulating varnish to a winding and, when required, baking to cure the varnish.

impressed. Forced upon or made to act.

impulse. A momentary increase in the current or voltage in a circuit.

incandescence. The glowing whiteness of a body caused by intense heat.

in phase. Two alternating quantities are said to be in phase when there is no phase difference between them, that is, when the angle of phase difference equals zero. Thus, the current is said to be in phase with the pressure when it neither leads nor lags.

incandescence, electric. The glowing of a substance when heated white hot by an electric current. Incandescence is produced by the passage of a current of high intensity through a conductor of high resistance.

incandescent lamp. An electric lighting device widely used and which lends itself to the greatest variety of uses. It operates on the principle of heating a wire to a white heat by sending an electric current through it. In construction, a slender filament of some conducting refractory material is enclosed in a glass chamber and connected to lead wires fused through the base of the chamber or "bulb". The bulb is exhausted of air as completely as possible and the exhaustion duct sealed. The object of placing the filament in a vacuum is to prevent oxidation.

inching. Electrically actuated angular movement or slow rotation of a machine, usually for maintenance or inspection.

inch pound. In mechanics, a unit of calculation; one pound lifted one inch.

incombustible material. Material that will not ignite or actively support combustion in a surrounding temperature of 1200 degrees F during an exposure of 5 minutes; also, material that will not melt when the temperature of the material is maintained at 900 degrees F for a period of at least 5 minutes.

incomplete circuit. A broken or open circuit.

independent ballast. A ballast that can be mounted separately outside a lighting fitting or fixture.

independent contact. A contacting member designed to close one circuit only.

India rubber. An elastic gummy substance derived from the milky juice of a variety of tropical trees and plants. India rubber has valuable insulating properties and is largely used in covering cables, etc.

indicating control switch. A switch that indicates its last control operation.

indicating device circuit. Circuit to which indicating devices are connected.

indicating fuse. A fuse that automatically indicates that the fuse has interrupted the circuit.

indicating instruments. Various DC and AC meters such as ammeters, voltmeters, wattmeters, etc.

indicating lamp. A lamp in an electric circuit which is designed to indicate varying conditions of the circuit by the quality of its own light.

indicating switch. A switch which indicates whether its circuit is open or closed.

indicator light. Any light, either incandescent or L.E.D., which indicates the status of a system.

indirect lighting. A method of lighting in which all of the light emitted from the unit is thrown first to the ceiling and from there diffused throughout the room. In such a system the ceiling acts as the light source, and the glare is reduced to a minimum. The resulting illumination is softer and more diffused and the shadows are less prominent.

indoor. Describing any equipment that is not sufficiently weather-resistant to permit outdoor use on a permanent basis.

indoor pothead. A pothead intended for use where the pothead insulator is protected from the weather.

indoor transformer. A non-weatherproof transformer.

induced. Brought about by induction, as when a body receives an electric charge by the influence upon it of a neighboring charged body.

induced current. An electric current set up in a circuit by cutting lines of force; a current caused by electro-magnetic induction; as, in an induction coil when the strength of a current flowing through the primary winding varies, magnetic changes take place in the core and surrounding field which induce currents in the other or secondary windings.

induced voltage. A voltage produced in a closed path or circuit by a change in magnetic flux linking that path.

inductance. The property of an electric circuit by virtue of which a varying current induces an electromotive force in that circuit or in a neighboring circuit. The property of a circuit which tends to oppose a change in the existing current.

induction. The process by which an electrical conductor becomes electrified when near a charged body and becomes magnetized.

induction motor. An AC motor in which energy from the stationary windings is transferred to conductors on the rotor by electromagnetic induction, and in which the rotor receives no current through any conductive contacts.

inductive circuit. A circuit containing more inductive reactance than capacitive reactance; such as one with many devices having iron core coils and windings; induction motors, etc.

inductive coupling. A form in which energy is transferred from a coil in one circuit to a coil in another by induction.

125

inductive load. A load in which the current lags behind the voltage across the load.

inductive rating. The maximum amount of amperes in a circuit when a conductor is in an electromagnetic field.

inductive reactance. The opposition to the flow of alternating current caused by the induction of a circuit. It is measured in ohms.

inductor. A coil, with or without an iron core, which opposes changes in current because of its self-inductance.

industrial control. The methods and means of governing the performance of an electric device, equipment, apparatus, or system used in the industry.

inertia. A property of matter by which it remains at rest or in uniform motion in the same straight line unless acted upon by some external force. As electricity, an analogous property of other physical quantities external force.

inflection. The bending of rays of light or radiant energy by defraction when passing by a sharp edge.

influence. A term used at times signifying electrostatic induction.

infrared detector. The passive type is one that detects an intruder by his body heat.

inherent motor protection. A safety-limit device built inside a motor or equipment. It protects for overtemperature, overcurrent, or both.

inhibit. To prevent an event from taking place; to prevent a device from producing a specified output.

initialize. To set counters and switches to zero or other starting values at the beginning of or at prescribed points in a computer routine.

initial voltage, battery. The closed-circuit voltage at the beginning of discharge.

inner frame. The portion of a frame in which the core and stator windings are mounted, which can be inserted and removed from an outer frame as a unit, without disturbing the mounting on the foundation.

inphase. Applied to the condition that exists when two waves of the same frequency pass through their maximum and minimum values of like polarity at the same instant.

input. The intake or energy absorbed by a machine during its operation, as distinguished from the output of useful energy delivered by it.

input current. The current absorbed by any electrical machine or device as indicated by an ammeter reading, as for instance the amperes taken by a motor.

input windings. The winding(s) to which the input is applied.

in sight from. Where the Code specifies that one equipment shall be "in sight from," etc., of another equipment, one of the equipments specified is to be visible and not more than a distance of 50 feet from the other.

installation test. A test made upon the consumer's premises within a limited period of time after installation.

instantaneous. A qualifying term used in giving properties and characteristics of apparatus indicating that no delay is purposely introduced in its action. Done in an instant.

instantaneous current. The strength of an electric current existing in a circuit at a given instant.

instantaneous trip circuit breaker. A qualifying term indicating that no delay is purposely introduced in the tripping action of the circuit breaker. Magnetic trip instead of thermal.

instantaneous value. The value of a variable quantity at a given instant.

instant-starting system, fluorescent lamps. A system in which an electric-discharge lamp is started by the application to the lamp of a voltage sufficiently high to eject electrons from the electrodes by field emission, initiate electron flow through the lamp, ionize the gases, and start a discharge through the lamp without previous heating of the electrodes.

instrument. (a) A measuring device such as a voltmeter, etc. Its measurements may be either indicating or recording. (b) A measuring device which measures the preset value of the quantity under observation. The term instrument is used in two different senses: (a) Instrument proper; (b) Any necessary apparatus, such as shunts, shunt leads, resistors, reactors, condensers or instrument transformers.

instrument relay. A relay whose operation depends upon principles employed in measuring instruments such as the electrodynamometer, iron vane, D'Arsonval galvanometer, and moving magnet.

instrument switch. A switch used to connect or disconnect an instrument or to transfer it from one circuit or phase to another.

instrument transformer. A form of transformer suitable for use with measuring instruments in which the conditions of current, pressure, and phase in the primary or high voltage circuit are represented with acceptable accuracy in the secondary or low voltage circuit. Current transformers are supplied to reduce the line current by a definite ratio so that a 5 ampere instrument may be used. They also serve to insulate the instrument from the voltage of the line, and should always be selected so that their voltage rating covers the voltage on which they are to be used. Potential transformers are used to reduce the line voltage by a definite ratio so that the instruments having a nominal voltage range of 150 volts may be used.

128

insulated. Separated from other conducting surfaces by a dielectric substance or air space permanently offering a high resistance to the passage of current and to disruptive discharge through the substance or space.

insulated conductor. A conductor encased within material of composition and thickness that is recognized by the Code as electrical insulation.

insulated pliers. Pliers provided with handles, covered with insulating material.

insulating material. A substance or body, the conductivity of which is zero or, in practice, very small.

insulating paint. A paint that is unaffected by an electric current; it is made of fossil gum, a pigment, and a vehicle, usually spirit of naphtha.

insulating tape. Tape, usually adhesive, rendered insulating by being saturated with an insulating compound, for the purpose of covering stripped ends and other exposed parts of insulated electric conductors.

insulation. Material having a tremendously high resistance, so placed with respect to a conductor, as to practically prevent leakage of current. Good insulating materials are: Oils, porcelain, plastics, rubber, resin, bakelite, glass.

insulation resistance. The ohmic resistance in an electric circuit offered by an insulating coating, cover, material or support to an impressed voltage, tending to produce a leakage of current through the same. By testing this resistance, a ready means is afforded of locating a fault in the insulation.

insulation-resistance test. A test for measuring the ohmic resistance of insulation at predetermined values of temperature and applied direct voltage.

insulation shielding. Conducting and/or semiconducting elements applied directly over and in intimate contact with the outer surface of the insulation.

insulator. A device for fastening and supporting a conductor. Glass and porcelain are employed almost universally for supporting overhead wires.

integral coupling. A coupling flange that is part of a shaft and not a separate piece.

integrated circuit. When transistors are packed together in a tiny chip, it is called an integrated circuit. Thousands of transistors can be packed together in one integrated chip that is no bigger than the smallest fingernail. Theses circuits are found in computers, televisions, etc.

integrator. A device which automatically counts or adds up items of calculation or measurement.

intensity of current. The strength of an electric current. It is the quantity of electricity that flows past any point in a circuit in one second, and is measured by a unit called the ampere. The intensity of a current has to do only with the amperage and must be considered apart from the pressure or voltage.

intercepted arc. The part of the circumference between the intersection of two lines with the circumference.

intercrossing. The cross system of running overhead wires to counteract the tendency to induction, in which the wires are crossed at intervals so as to change their relation to one another.

interface. A shared boundary.

interference. Either extraneous power, that tends to interfere with the reception of the desired signals, or the disturbance of signals that results.

interior conduit. A conduit suitable for use in walls or floors of a building for the accomodation of electric wires.

interlock. A device actuated by the operation of some other device with which it is directly associated, to govern succeeding operations of the same or allied devices.

interlock relay. A relay with two or more armatures having a mechanical linkage, or an electric interconnection, or both, whereby the position of one armature permits, prevents, or causes motion of another armature.

intermediate contacts. Contacts in the main circuit that part after the main contacts and before the arcing contacts have parted.

intermittent. Ceasing to act at intervals. Fluctuating.

intermittent current. An electric current that starts and stops at regular intervals. Such current is obtained by placing in the circuit some type of interrupter as a vibrator. The mechanism of an electric bell is so arranged as to supply an intermittent current to the magnets.

intermittent duty. Operation for alternate intervals of (1) load and no load; or (2) load and rest; or (3) load, no load, and rest. A requirement of operation or service consisting of alternate periods of load and rest so apportioned and regulated that the temperature rise at no time exceeds that specified for the particular class of apparatus under consideration.

intermittent fault. A fault that recurrs in the same place and due to the same cause within a short period of time.

intermittent pilot. A pilot lit each time the thermostat demands heat. When the thermostat is satisfied, the pilot light and main burner are turned off at the same time.

internal connector. A connector that joins the end of the cable to the other current-carrying parts of a pothead.

internal heating. The electrolysis of fused electrolytes is the method of maintaining the electrolyte in a molten condition by the heat generated by the passage of current through the electrolyte.

internal overload. A protective device placed inside the motor winding at a predetermined place to protect the motor from overheat, overcurrent, or both.

internal resistance. The resistance to the flow of an electric current within a cell or battery.

interphase transformer. An autotransformer, or a set of mutually coupled reactors, used to obtain parallel operation between two or more simple rectifiers that have ripple voltages that are out of phase.

interpolation. A function that may be used to obtain additional values between sampled values.

interpole. A small auxiliary pole introduced between two main field poles of a motor or dynamo in order to produce a compensating field under heavy loads; a compensating or commutating pole.

interpole motor. A DC motor which has in addition to the main poles, a series of interpoles, placed between the main poles. The object of these poles is to provide an auxiliary flux or "commutating" field at the point where the armature coils are short-circuited by the brush.

interrupt. To stop a process in such a way that it can be resumed.

interrupted. Broken in upon; having the continuity of the circuit broken; as, by a contact breaker.

interrupter switch. An air switch, equipped with an interrupter, for making or breaking specified currents, or both.

intrinsically safe apparatus. Apparatus in which any spark or thermal effect produced, either normally or in specified fault conditions, is incapable of causing ignition of a mixture of flammable or combustible material in air in its most easily ignitible concentration. This apparatus is suitable for use in Division 1 locations.

intrinsically safe circuit. A circuit in which any spark or thermal effect produced, either normally or in specified fault conditions, is incapable of causing ignition of a mixture of flammable or combustible material in air in its most easily ignited concentration.

inverse. Opposite in order, nature, or effect.

inverse current. A current produced in a conductor when a current is started or strengthened in a parallel conductor which has a parallel component. The current produced in an induction coil when the circuit of the primary is making or completing.

inverse electrode current. The current flowing through an electrode in the direction opposite to that for which the tube is designed.

inverse ratio. That formed by inverting the terms of a given ratio; thus, 5:6 is the inverse of 6:5.

inverse-square law. A statement that the strength of the field due to a point source or the irradiance from a point source decreases as the square of the distance from the source.

inverse time (as applied to circuit breakers). A qualifying term indicating there is purposely introduced a delay in the tripping action of the circuit breaker, which delay decreases as the magnitude of the current increases.

inverse-time relay. A relay in which the input quantity and operating time are inversely related throughout at least a substantial portion of the performance range.

inverse voltage (rectifier). The voltage applied between the two terminals in the direction opposite to the forward direction. This direction is called the backward direction.

inverter. Equipment which changes direct current to alternating current.

ion. An electrically charged atom or radical.

ionization. The process of electrically charging neutral atoms or molecules either positively or negatively.

ions. The products of electrolysis which appear at the electrodes; the component which appears at the anode is called the anion, or electronegative component, and that which appears at the cathode is called the cation or electropositive component.

IR drop. The reduction or "drop" in voltage due to an increase in resistance of a conductor caused by the heating effect of a current flowing in a conductor.

I^2R loss. The power consumed by the heating effect of a current passing through a conductor. It is equal to the square of the current times the resistance.

iron. One of the metallic elements. It is obtained from ores in which it is combined with earthy or stony substances and frequently with carbon, phosphorus, sulphur, arsenic, magnesia, etc. Carbon decreases the permeability, increases coercive force and hysteresis losses and also increases the electrical resistance of the iron.

iron clad. Covered with, or clad in iron, as an iron clad magnet.

iron loss in transformer. The loss of energy sustained by a transformer by reason of magnetic hysteresis or friction, and also due to the establishment of eddy or Foucault currents in iron.

isochronous speed governing. Governing with steady-state speed regulation of essentially zero magnitude.

isogonic line. An imaginary line drawn through points on the earth's surface where the magnetic deviation is equal.

isolated. Not readily accessible to persons unless special means for access are used.

isolated by elevation. Elevated sufficiently so that persons may walk safely underneath.

isolated conductor. In a multiple conductor system, a conductor either accessible or inaccessible, the charge of which is not changed and to which no connection is made in the course of the determination of any one of the capacitances of the remaining conductors of the system.

isolated-neutral system. A system that has no intentional connection to ground except through indicating, measuring, or protective devices of very high impedance.

isolating switch. A switch whereby an electric lamp may be cut out of a circuit without affecting the other lamps on that circuit.

isolation. Electrical separation between two locations.

isolation voltage. The maximum withstand potential at 60 hertz between live parts and metal mounting surface of the semiconductor.

isometric projection. A method of perspective drawing of mechanical objects. It enables three sides to be seen at one view, being a projection on lines equally inclined to the three principal axis of the object delineated, the angles remaining the same as in plane drawing.

isotope. Isotope is an atom that has the same number of protons but a different number of neutrons than the usual atoms of an element.

J

jack. A connecting device, ordinarily designed for use in a fixed location, to which a wire or wires of a circuit may be attached and that is arranged for the insertion of a plug.

jacket. A device having sleeves.

jacket, cable. A thermoplastic covering, sometimes fabric reinforced, applied over the insulation, core, metallic sheath, or armor of a cable.

jack screw. A device for raising heavy weights, in which the power of the screw is applied.

jack shaft. A separate shaft carried on its own bearings and connected to the shaft of a machine.

Jacobi's law. A law of electric motors which states that the maximum work of a motor is performed when its counter electromotive force is equal to one-half the electromotive force expended on the motor.

jag bolt. A tail bolt whose shank or tail is roughed up by jagging.

jamb. Upright member forming the side of a door or window opening.

jam nut. A nut placed in contact with the main nut on the same bolt to keep the main nut from turning.

japan. A variety of enamel sometimes used for the insulation of electrical machines, as when the smooth core of an armature is japanned to increase the insulation of the conductors from the iron body.

jar, electric. The Leyden jar, an early form of electric condenser. It consists of a wide mouthed glass cylindrical vessel coated inside and out, up to a certain distance from the top, with tin foil.

jaw. The stationary contact member of a switch.

jenny pole support. Two legs of suitable length pivoted near one end and arranged so as to support a telegraph or power wire pole during erection.

jog (inch). A control function that provides for the momentary operation of a drive for the purpose of accomplishing a small movement of the driven machine.

jogging. The quickly repeated closure of the circuit to start a motor from rest for the purpose of accomplishing small movements of the driven machine.

joining up. The act or process of making an electrical connection.

joint. The tying together of two single wire conductors so that the union will be good, both mechanically and electrically.

jointing. The process of uniting the end of two single wire conductors. The word joint is commonly used incorrectly for splice.

joule. A measure of electrical energy; a power of one watt for one second; the work done by sending one ampere through a resistance of one ohm for one second.

joulean heat. The heat due to the work performed by an electric current in overcoming the resistance of the circuit in which it flows.

joule effect. The heat produced by the resistance offered by a conductor to the flow of an electric current.

Joule's law. The law first stated by Joule, that the quantity of heat developed in a conductor by the passage of an electric current is proportional to the resistance of the conductor, to the square of the strength of the current, and to the duration of the flow.

journal. A cylindrical section of a shaft that is intended to rotate inside a bearing.

journal bearing. A bearing that supports the cylindrical journal of a shaft.

journeyman. An experienced reliable workman in any field.

jumper. A wire used as temporary connection.

junction. A point in a parallel or series-parallel circuit where current branches off into two or more paths.

junction box. A box with a blank cover that serves the purpose of joining different runs of raceway or cable and provides space for the connection and branching of the enclosed conductors.

jute. The coarse strong fiber of an East Indian plant largely used for gunny sacks, cordage, etc. In the electrical practice, jute is employed as an insulating material, especially when saturated with an insulating compound.

K

K. The symbol for dielectric constant.

kaolin. A variety of clay serviceable for insulating.

keeper. The armature of a magnet; the bar of soft iron placed across the poles of a horseshoe magnet to prevent loss of magnetism.

key. A hand-operated switching device ordinarily comprising concealed spring contacts with an exposed handle or pushbutton, capable of switching one or more parts of a circuit.

keyless wall socket. A lamp socket fitted to a wall having terminals to which the flexible wires leading to the lamp are connected by a plug block.

kick. A recoil.

kick box. In house wiring, a fitting for protecting wires at the points where they enter or emerge from the floor.

kick of coil. A discharge from an electromagnetic coil.

killing wire. (a) A method of straightening wire by applying tension to it. (b) The loss of elasticity suffered by the contact springs of switches when heated to excess by the electric current.

kilo. A prefix often used with a physical unit to designate a quantity one thousand times as great.

kilo-ampere. A unit of current, equal to 1,000 amperes.

kilovolt (kv). A unit of pressure equal to one thousand volts.

kilovolt-ampere (kva). The unit of apparent power in alternating current circuits as distinguished from kilowatts which represent the true power.

kilovolt-ampere rating. The product of the rated load amperes and the kilovolts. For three-phase, amperes times voltage times 1.732.

kilowatt. A unit of electric power, equal to one thousand watts. Electric power is usually expressed in kilowatts. As the watt is equal to 1/746 horsepower, the kilowatt or 1,000 watts = 1.34 hp. Careful distinction should be made between kilowatts and kilovolt amperes.

kilowatt hour. The work performed by one kilowatt of electric power during an hour's time.

kilowatt hour meter. A type of recording wattmeter measuring in terms of kilowatt hours (kwh).

kinebooth. A fireproof room of approved construction in which motion picture projectors, spotlights, and auxiliary equipment are located. The word kinebooth has been adopted and accepted by architects and engineers to define that particular section of a building.

kinematics. (a) That branch of mechanics which treats of motion without reference to mass or to the causes of motion, as distinguished from dynamics. (b) The theory of the motions of parts of machines whereby they are constrained to fulfill their various functions, one variety of motion being employed to produce another.

kinetics. The science which treats of motions considered in themselves or apart from their causes.

kinetic energy. The energy of a moving body by virtue of its momentum.

king leg. The principal or vertical leg of a tripod supporting a derrick, etc; the other legs are known as the queen legs.

Kirchoff's current law. The sum of all currents flowing to a point in a circuit must be equal to the sum of all currents flowing away from that point.

Kirchoff's laws. (a) The algebraic sum of the currents flowing toward any point in a network is zero. (b) The algebraic sum of the products of the current and resistance in each of the conductors in any closed path in a network is equal to the algebraic sum of the voltages in that path.

Kirchoff's voltage law. Sum of all voltage sources acting in a complete circuit must be equal to the sum of all the voltage drops in the circuit.

knife switch. A switch in which one or more metal blades (usually copper), pivoted at one end, serve as the moving parts.

knob and tube wiring. Wiring especially for lighting circuits, supported by knobs and tubes. It may be concealed between floors or walls of buildings or exposed. Knob and tube wiring should be discouraged as often as possible, as it is subject to mechanical injury, is liable to interference from rats, mice, etc. As the wires run according to this method are liable to sag against beams, laths, etc., or are likely to be covered by shavings or other flammable building material, a fire could easily result if the wires become overheated or short circuited. Before installing concealed knob and tube wiring it should first be ascertained if this method is permitted by the local code.

knockout. A scored portion in the wall of a box or cabinet which can be easily removed by striking with a hammer; a circular hole is provided thereby for accommodation of conduit or cable.

knockout, concentric. Several discs having a common center.

knockout, eccentric. Discs not having the same center; deviating from a circular path.

kva. Kilovolt-amperes, the product of volts and amperes divided by 1,000.

141

L

L. The symbol for inductance.

label. An adhesive backed construction, bearing printing or capable to bearing printing.

labeled. Equipment or materials to which has been attached a label, symbol, or other identifying mark of an organization acceptable to the authority having jurisdiction and concerned with product evaluation, that maintains periodic inspection of production of labeled equipment or materials and by whose labeling, the manufacturer indicates compliance with appropriate standards or performance in a specified manner.

lag. That condition where the phase of one AC quantity lags behind that of another. The term is generally used in connection with the effect of inductance in causing the current to lag behind the impressed voltage. Lag is measured in degrees that is in actual alternation. If the current lag is 45 degrees behind the pressure, it means that the coil rotates 45 degrees from its position of zero induction before the current starts. The angle of lag may have any value from 0 to 90 degrees.

lag and lead. Alternating currents do not always keep in step with the alternating volts impressed upon the circuit. If there is inductance in the circuit, the current will lag; if there is capacity, the current will lead in phase.

lagging current. The retardation of an alternating current behind the impressed voltage which produces it. Inductance causes the current to lag below the pressure in that it tends to prevent changes in the strength of the current. When two parts of a circuit are near each other, so that one is in the magnetic field of the other, any change in the strength of the current causes a corresponding change in the magnetic field and sets up a reverse pressure in the other wire. This induced pressure causes the current to reach its maximum value a little later than the pressure.

lally column. Compression member consisting of a steel pipe filled with concrete under pressure.

lambert. A unit of luminance.

Lambert's cosine law. A law stating that the flux per solid angle in any direction from a plane surface varies as the cosine of the angle between that direction and the perpendicular to the surface.

laminate. To beat, roll, or press into thin sheets, as a metal.

laminated brush. A contact part consisting of thin sheets of conducting material fastened together so as to secure individual contact by the edges of the separate sheets.

laminated core. An armature core built up of layers of insulated iron plates in order to prevent the formation of Foucault currents in the metal.

lamination. A relatively thin member, usually made of sheet material. A complete structure is made by assembling the laminations in the required number of layers. In a core that carries alternating magnetic flux, the core material is usually laminated to reduce eddy-current losses.

lamp. The device, commonly called a "light bulb" or "bulb", intended to be inserted into a lampholder ("socket") to produce light.

lamp base. The brass base which is cemented by plaster to the bulb of an incandescent lamp, and which contains the contacts for bringing the filament into connection with the electric current.

lamp bulb. The glass vacuum chamber containing the filament of an incandescent lamp; the lamp chamber.

lamp cord. Two-conductor, parallel construction, #18 gauge wire typically used on 120 volt floor and table lamps and in light-duty extension cords.

143

lamp dimmer. A variable resistance connected in series with incandescent lamps to reduce the brightness or the light output to a desired value.

lamp, electric. A lamp which depends for its source of light upon the effects of an electric current. Electric lamps may be grouped into three classes: (1) incandescent lamps in which the source of light is the incandescence of a refractory substance upon the passage of a current; (2) arc lamps in which a luminous arc is maintained by an electric current between suitable electrodes, and (3) vapor lamps in which the vapor in an exhausted glass tube becomes an incandescent stream of high conductivity.

lamp filament. The conducting thread which becomes incandescent upon the passage of an electric current in an incandescent lamp.

lampholder. A screw-shell device for receiving the screw base of a lamp bulb or other part; a lamp socket.

lampholder adapter. A device, that by insertion in a receptacle, serves as a lampholder.

lamp pendant. The lamp cord used in connection with a pendant incandescent lamp.

lamp post. A standard support provided with the necessary internal attachments for wiring and the external attachments for the bracket and luminaire.

lamp socket. The socket provided with contacts, into which the base of an incandescent lamp is designed to fit; the lamp receptacle.

lanthanum. A rare metal belonging to the same group as aluminum.

lap joint. A wire joint in which the two ends are laid side by side, bound together, and soldered. The Britannia joint is an example.

lap winding. An armature winding in which the ends of the coils come back to adjacent segments of the commutator; the coils of such a winding lap over each other.

laser. The name stands for "Light Amplification by Simulated Emission of Radiation". The laser emits an almost perfect parallel beam. A remarkable piece of electrical equipment used today by scientists, doctor's, as well as the industry.

latching relay. A relay that is so constructed that it maintains a given position by means of a mechanical latch until released mechanically or electrically.

latent. Not visible or apparent. Hidden.

latent heat. The quantity of heat which may be added to a substance during a change of state without causing a temperature change.

lateral conductor. A wire or cable extending sideways or at an angle to the general direction of the line.

laundry on premises. A laundry facility on the property available to all tenants; an apartment complex laundromat.

laws of electrical resistance. (a) The resistance of a conducting wire is proportional to its length. (b) The resistance of a conducting wire is inversely proportional to the area of its cross section, and therefore in the usual round wires, is inversely proportional to the square of its diameter. (c) The resistance of a conducting wire of given length and thickness depends upon the material of which it is made; that is, upon the specific resistance of the material. (d) The resistance in general increases with the temperature.

laws of electromagnetic induction. There are certain laws of electromagnetic induction which, on account of the importance of the subject, it is well to carefully consider the following: (a) Faraday's discovery: To induce a current in a circuit, there must be a relative motion between the circuit and a magnetic field, of such a kind as to alter the number of magnetic lines embraced in the circuit. (b) The voltage or current induced in a circuit is proportional to the rate of increase or decrease in the number of magnetic lines embraced by the circuit. (c) When a straight wire cuts 100,000,000 lines of force at right angles per second, an electric pressure of one volt is induced. (d) By joining in series a number of inductors or coils moving in a magnetic field, the electric pressures in the separate parts are added together. (e) A decrease in the number of magnetic lines which pass through a circuit induces a current around the circuit in the positive direction. (f) An increase in the number of magnetic lines which pass through a circuit induces a current in the negative direction around the circuit. (g) The approach and recession of a conductor from a magnet pole will yield currents alternating in direction. (h) The more rapid the motion, the higher will be the induced voltage. (i) Lenz's law. The direction of the induced current is always such that its magnetic field opposes the motion which produces it.

laws of heat. Heat is transmitted is three ways: (a) by conduction, as when the end of a short rod of iron is placed in a fire, and the opposite end becomes warm, this is conducted heat; (b) by convection, such as warming of a mass of water in a boiler, and (c) by radiation, as that diffused from a piece of hot metal or an open fire. Radiant heat is transmitted, like sound or light, in straight lines in every direction, and its intensity diminishes inversely as the square of the distance from its center of radiation.

laws of magnetic force. (a) Like magnetic poles repel one another, unlike magnetic poles attract one another. (b) The force exerted between two magnetic poles varies inversely as the square of the distance between them.

lay. The length of one complete turn in multiple wires or cables. For example: One inch lay in twisted pair is one complete twist per inch.

lay of wires. The manner in which wires are caused to make a complete twist about a central core or axis.

lead. (a) That condition where the phase on one alternating quantity is in advance of the other. The term is generally used in connection with the effect of capacity in causing the current to lead or be in advance of the pressure. Lead is measured in degrees; that is, in alternation. If the current lead is 45 degrees in advance of the pressure, it means that the current starting position of zero induction when the coil is 45 degrees in position. Lead may vary from 0 to 90 degrees. (b) An insulated conducting wire which leads from an electric source to any main, feeder, station, instrument, circuit, etc. In general, one of the conductors in a system of electric distribution.

lead (alloy). A lustrous, blue-gray metal, soft enough to be cut with a knife or to leave a mark on a piece of paper; it is malleable and ductile, but it is not a good conductor of heat and electricity compared with other metals.

lead cable. A cable type of conductor connected to the stator winding, used for making connections to the supply line or other circuits of the stator winding.

lead-covered cable. A cable provided with a sheath of lead for the purpose of excluding moisture and affording mechanical protection.

lead-in. That portion of an antenna system that connects the elevated conductor portion to the radio equipment.

leading current. AC current (in a capacitive circuit) whose zero values and maximum values in a given direction occur before the zeros and corresponding maximums of the AC voltage in the same circuit.

leading in wires. Conductors leading from an overhead circuit into a building.

lead of current. When the capacity of an AC circuit is more effective than the induction, the current leads the pressure.

lead storage battery. A storage battery, the electrodes of which are made of lead, and the electrolyte consists of a solution of sulfuric acid.

leaf switch. A mechanical switch sometimes used on windows or doors that is actuated by a long, narrow strip of springy metal (leaf) extending from the switch body.

leakage. The escape of electric current through defects in insulation or other causes.

leakage, surface. Passage of current over the boundary surfaces of an insulator as distinguished from passage of current through its bulk.

leathers. In hydraulics, cup or hat leathers are used in pumps or hydraulic presses.

LED. Abbreviation for light emitting diode.

left-handed rotation. Movement of a rotating body in a direction from right to left, or in the opposite direction of the hands of a clock as they are seen to move when one reads time counter-clockwise rotation.

leg. Any one of the conductors of an electric supply circuit between which is maintained the maximum supply voltage.

leg of circuit. A branch or lateral circuit connected with the main circuit.

lens. A piece of glass or other transparent substance with one or both sides curved. Both sides may be curved and the other flat. The object of a lens is to change the direction of rays of light, and thus magnify objects, or otherwise modify vision. That is, it causes the rays to converge or diverge in passing through the lens.

Lenz's law. The direction of the induced current is always such that its magnetic field opposes the motion which produces it.

lever switch. A type of switch for light duty. Its distinguishing feature is that the blade, pivoted at one end and operated by a handle at the other end, swings in a plane parallel with the base. A switch of this type, if placed vertically, should be in such a position that gravity tends to open the circuit.

Leyden jar condenser. A type of condenser consisting of a glass jar coated inside and out to a certain height with tinfoil, having a brass rod terminating in a knob passed through a wooden stopper, and connected to the inner coat by a loose chain. Used in making static electricity experiments.

life of lamp. The number of burning hours for which a lamp is specifically designed. This life varies with the service, and for tungsten filament lamps bears a definite relation to the light ouput of the lamp. In general, it can be said that if the life be lengthened the light output will be decreased, and if the life be shortened, the light output will be increased. The most economic life of a lamp is determined by considering the cost of the lamp, the cost of making renewals, and the cost of power per unit of light output consumed throughout life.

life test of lamps. A test in which lamps are operated under specified conditions for a specified length of time, for the purpose of obtaining information on lamp life.

lifting magnets. A type of magnet used in connection with power operated cranes and hoists, for lifting magnetic material, especially where such material must be handled in bulk.

light. That form of radiant energy which affects the eye so that objects become visible.

light cell. A name sometimes given to a photoelectric cell.

lighting branch circuits. Circuits supplying energy to lighting outlets only.

lighting feeder. A feeder supplying principally a lighting load.

lighting mains. In an electric lighting system of house wiring, the conductors which are prolongations of the "feeders". They run from the outside lines to the distribution center.

lighting outlet. An outlet intended for the direct connection of a lampholder, a lighting fixture, or a pendant cord terminating in a lampholder.

lightness. The attribute by which an object seems to transmit or reflect a greater or lesser fraction of the incident light.

lightning. An electric discharge in the atmosphere from cloud to cloud, between cloud and earth or within a cloud. When such a discharge between cloud and earth terminates on a transmission line, a distribution line, electric machinery or other objects, it is called a direct stroke of lightning. Although direct strokes may be destructive, they usually strike electrical systems only in the transmission circuit.

lightning arrester. (a) A device for providing a path by which lightning disturbances or other static discharges are passed to earth. A lightning arrester is a device intended primarily to prevent damage to electrical apparatus which may be caused by disturbances due to lightning. There are numerous types. (b) A device providing a path for electric current between any electric circuit and the earth, through which, upon occurrence of a lightning surge, current will be conducted in sufficient amount to reduce the over voltage of the circuit caused by the surge, and after this reduction, the current will cease to be so conducted.

150

lightning bolt. The flash of a discharge of lightning.

lightning jar. A Leyden jar coated with metallic filings which exhibit scintillating sparks when the jar is discharged.

lightning outage. A power outage following a lightning flashover that results in power follow current, necessitating the operation of a switching device to clear the fault.

lightning rod. A conducting rod or cable erected on the outside of a building and connected to earth, in order to afford protection from lightning by carrying the lightning discharge into the ground; or to prevent lightning by leading the electricity from the earth to the cloud without disturbance.

lightning stroke. A single lightning discharge or series of discharges following the same path between cloud regions or between cloud regions and the earth.

lightning surge. A transient electric disturbance in an electric circuit caused by lightning.

lillie wire joint. A method of joining wires in which the connector consists of a strip of copper curved longitudinally in opposite directions, the wires being slipped into the curved channels and twisted in opposite directions.

limelight. The oxyhydrogen flame or calcium light. Hydrogen burns in air with a nonluminous hot flame. If it burns in combination with oxygen instead of with air, the heat is greatly intensified. By allowing this flame to impinge upon a small cylinder of lime (calcium oxide) an exceedingly brilliant light results.

limit switch. A switch that is operated by some part or motion of a driven machine or equipment to alter the electric circuit associated with the machine or equipment.

line. In general, a conducting wire between stations in a system of electric communication or distribution.

line drop. The difference in voltage along a transmission line between two given points due to the resistance of the line between the two points.

linear capacity. A quantity equal to the capacity of a conductor divided by its length.

linear light. A luminous signal having a perceptible physical length.

linear measure. A measure of length. There are various measures of length, such as: Long measure, surveyors' or old land measure, nautical measure, etc.

line breaker. A device that combines the functions of a contactor and of a circuit breaker.

line conductor. One of the wires or cables carrying electric current, supported by poles, towers, or other structures.

line side. Ahead of the main overcurrent protective device.

lines of magnetic force. Lines assumed to exist in a magnetic field of force, tracing the paths along which magnetism acts. If a thin piece of paper is placed over a bar magnet and fine iron filings be sprinkled over it, the particles of iron will arrange themselves in regular curves between the poles and map out or define lines in a magnetic field which scientists call lines of force.

line starter. A motor starter which applies full line voltage to the motor immediately on operation of the starter.

line voltage. The voltage at a wall outlet or terminal of a power line system.

linkages. The linking together of lines of magnetic force and the conducting coils through which they pass; the total number of linkages being the product of the magnetic flux by the number of turns in a coil.

link fuse. A safety fuse containing a link of fusible material.

liquid level alarm. An electric alarm given by the action of a float upon a make and break mechanism, when a certain liquid falls below or exceeds a given level; a water level alarm.

liquid resistance. Pure water is sometimes employed for the control of the electric current. The water is usually contained in a wooden box called the "water box". Metal terminals are immersed in the water and the resistance is adjusted by varying the degree to which the terminals are immersed or by changing the distance between them. Liquid resistances are often convenient in connection with electrical testing.

liquids as conductors. With respect to the conducting properties of liquids, they may be divided into three classes: (1) those which are insulators, as turpentine, petroleum, and many oils; (2) those which conduct without decomposition, as mercury; and (3) those which conduct and are decomposed, as dilute acids and solutions of metallic salts, etc.

listed. Equipment or materials included in a list published by an organization acceptable to the authority having jurisdiction and concerned with product evaluation, that maintains periodic inspection of production of listed equipment or materials, and whose listing states either that the equipment or material meets appropriate standards or has been tested and found suitable for use in a specified manner.

litzendraht wire. A multistrand wire having transpositions to reduce skin effect.

live front switchboard. One having live parts on the front of the panels.

live parts. Those parts that are designed to operate at voltage different from that of earth.

live wire. A wire in actual use as a part of an electric circuit, especially one through which a strong current is passing.

load. The total of equipment or consuming devices connected to a battery, generator, or supply circuit; measured in watts, watt-hours, ohms, amperes, volts.

load center. A point at which the load of a given area is assumed to be concentrated.

load factor. The ratio of the average load to the maximum load.

load-interrupter switch. An interrupter switch designed to interrupt currents not in excess of the continuous current rating of the switch.

load limiting resistor. One which is used in a circuit for the purpose of reducing the current in that circuit to a safe value.

load losses of transformers. These are the losses in the windings due to load current, stray losses due to stray fluxes in the windings, core lamps, etc. and in some cases with parallel windings, losses due to circulating current.

load panel. In a system of electric distribution, a switchboard supplied with the devices for recording the electric output of the central station.

load rheostat. A rheostat whose sole purpose is to dissipate electric energy. Often used for load tests of generators.

loaded transformer. When the load on a transformer is increased, the primary of the transformer automatically takes additional current and power from the supply mains in direct proportion to the load on the secondary. When the load on the secondary is reduced, for example by turning off loads, the power taken from the supply mains by the primary coil is automatically reduced in proportion to the decrease in the load. This automatic action of the transformer is due to the balanced magnetizing action of the primary and secondary currents.

local lighting. Lighting that provides illumination over a relatively small area or confined space without providing any significant general surrounding lighting.

location, damp. Partially protected locations under canopies, marquees, roofed open porches, and like locations, and interior locations subject to moderate degrees of moisture, such as some basements, barns, and cold-storage warehouses.

location, dry. A location not normally subject to dampness or wetness. A location classified as dry may be temporarily subject to dampness or wetness, as in the case of a building under construction.

location, wet. Installations underground or in concrete slabs or masonry, in direct contact with the earth and locations subject to saturation with water or other liquids, such as vehicle washing areas, and locations exposed to weather and unprotected.

locked rotor. The condition existing when the motor circuit is energized but the rotor is not turning.

locked rotor current. The steady-state current taken from the line with the rotor locked and with rated voltage applied to the motor.

locked rotor torque. Minimum torque of a motor developed at rest for any position of the rotor with full voltage.

locking relay. One which renders some other relay or other device inoperative under predetermined values of current or voltage, etc.

locknut. An internally threaded fitting for use on rigid conduit or fittings to prevent turning and to provide a secure joint.

locking relay. One which renders some other relay or other inoperative under predetermined values of current or voltage, etc.

locknut. An internally threaded fitting for use on rigid conduit or fittings to prevent turning and to provide a secure joint.

lockout relay. An electrically reset or hand-reset auxiliary relay whose function is to hold associated devices inoperative until it is reset.

lodestone. A variey of magnetite, or the magnetic oxide of iron, possessing in a natural state the properties of a magnet; a natural magnet.

logarithm. The power to which a given invariable number called the base must be raised in order to produce that number.

logarithmic curve. A curve in which the ordinate's rate of increase or decrease is proportional to itself.

loop bracket. A bracket with one or more insulators at a point where a loop is introduced into a circuit; a spreader bracket.

loop circuit. A branched or parallel circuit.

loop system of distribution. An early method of distribution in an electric lighting system in which each lamp obtained its current through a separate circuit of its own.

loop test. A method of testing employed to locate a fault in the insulation of a conductor when the conductor can be arranged to form part of a closed circuit or loop.

loss. Power expended without accomplishing useful work.

losses. I²R loss in the windings, core loss, dielectric loss, or losses due to stray magnetic fluxes in the windings.

loss factor. The ratio of the average power loss to the peak lead power loss during a specified period of time.

loudness. The intensive attribute of an auditory sensation in terms of which sound may be ordered on a scale extending from soft to loud.

louver window. A window consisting of many slats of glass each about 3 or 4 inches wide that all open simultaneously by a crank.

low-energy power circuit. A circuit that is not a remote control or signal circuit but that has a power supply limited in accordance with the requirements of Class 2 remote control circuits.

low frequency. A comparatively small number of complete cycles of vibration performed in a unit of time, 25 cycles as compared with 60 cycles.

low lagging power factor. In general, on systems where the power factor is low, the cause is almost entirely in induction motors. Unreasonably low power factors will usually be found due to: (1) the use of motors of inferior design and construction requiring larger magnetizing current than necessary; (2) the use of motors too large for the duty they perform; (3) the practice of allowing motors to run idle or lightly loaded.

low power factor. A condition which causes increased current for motors and higher energy losses in the distribution system. These wiring losses due to low power factor, in some cases, become extremely large when compared with the total energy required by the plant and in many cases the plant wiring is so taxed by the heavy current that it is too small to give satisfactory service.

low voltage protection. The effect of a device, operative on the reduction or failure of voltage, to cause and maintain the interruption of power supply to the equipment protected.

low voltage relay. Generally used for the protection of motors in the event of a temporary weakening or failure of the voltage. They are also used in connection with a low voltage release or shunt trip coil on an oil switch or a circuit breaker.

low voltage release. The effect of a device, operative on the reduction or failure of voltage, to cause the interruption of power supply to the equipment, but not preventing the re-establishment of the power supply on return of voltage.

lubrication. The theory of lubrication, is the interposition of a film of unguent between the two surfaces which are supposed to rub together by reason of the motion of one of them. The friction of the surfaces on the unguent is less than their friction on one another, so that lubrication lessens friction, saves power, and diminishes the risk of damage, wear, and tear.

lug. A fitting which connects a wire to the contact block of a switch.

lumen. The unit of luminous flux. The luminous flux emitted in a unit solid angle by a uniform point source of one international candle.

lumen-hour. The unit of quantity of light. One lumen continued for one hour.

luminaire. A complete lighting unit consisting of a lamp or lamps together with the parts designed to distribute the light, to position and protect the lamps, and to connect the lamps to the power supply.

luminance. Often referred to as brightness.

lux. The practical unit illumination, using the metric system of measurement; the illumination of a surface one square meter in area receiving an evenly distributed flux of one lumen.

M

M. Symbol for mutual inductance.

M. A value of multiplication by 1,000; 25M means 25,000.

machine. A term sometimes applied to rotative electrical apparatus signifying indeterminately a dynamo, alternator, motor, or converter, etc.

machine bolt. A bolt screwed at one end, with a head on the other, used to secure two pieces together, passing through clearance holes in both, and fastened with a nut on the far side. The head of a machine bolt is generally square or hexagonal, although round, snap, countersunk, or other heads are used for special purposes.

machine, electric. An electric apparatus depending on electromagnetic induction for its operation and having one or more component members capable of rotary and/or linear movement.

made circuit. A closed or completed circuit.

magazine fuse. A safety fuse provided with duplicate fuses in reserve, so that when one becomes burned out, a new fuse may readily be substituted.

magnesium cell. A primary cell with the negative electrode made of magnesium or its alloy.

magnet. A body possessing the property of attracting to itself particles of iron. A natural magnet is a piece of magnetite or magnetic oxide of iron which will attract other iron, will repel or attract similar magnets according to their relative positions, and when suspended so as to be free to turn, will set itself in a definite direction with respect to the earth's magnetic poles.

magnet coil. A conducting coil of insulated wire wound around the core of an electromagnet.

magnetic adherence. A tendency noticeable in bodies of iron to adhere to the poles of a magnet.

magnetic amplifier. A saturable reactor type device that is used in a circuit to amplify or control.

magnetic axis. The line which connects the poles of a magnet.

magnetic blowout. A magnet, often electrically excited, whose field is used to aid the interruption of an arc drawn between contacts.

magnetic circuit. The complete path of magnetic lines of force.

magnetic contactor. A contactor actuated by electromagnetic means.

magnetic control relay. A relay that is actuated by electromagnetic means.

magnetic core. A configuration of magnetic material that is, or is intended to be, placed in a rigid spatial relationship to current-carrying conductors and whose magnetic properties are essential to its use.

magnetic density. The number of lines of magnetic force passing through a magnet or magnetic field per unit area of cross section.

magnetic fatigue. The increase in the hysteretic coefficient of iron resulting from an assumed fatigue following numerous cyclic reversals.

magnetic field. The region, surrounding a magnet, through which magnetic forces act; the space around the magnet in which the compass needles or other detector of magnetism will be affected. The magnetic field is said to be comprised of lines of force. It is most intense near the poles of the magnet and as the distance from the magnet is increased, these lines of force become weaker and weaker, until they finally disappear.

magnetic flux. The average field intensity of a magnet multiplied by its area; its unit is the maxwell.

magnetic friction. A term sometimes applied to hysteresis.

magnetic hysteresis. The property of a ferromagnetic material exhibited by the lack of correspondence between the changes in induction resulting from increasing magnetizing force from decreasing magnetizing force.

magnetic induction. The strength of magnetism which is in an induced magnet, caused partly by the polarized particles of material which surround it and partly by the magnetic field. The density, in air, of magnetic force; and in all magnetic materials it is the sum of the magnetic force and the magnetic flux produced in the iron thereby. Total density of magnetic flux. Magnetization induced in a magnetizable substance when brought into magnetic flux.

magnetic inertia. The lack of power of a magnetic core to acquire or to part with its magnetism instantly.

magnetic lag. The tendency of a mass of iron to take up magnetism slowly. The tendency of an iron core to resist magnetism resulting in retardation. Magnetic retardation.

magnetic lines of force. Certain lines or directions in which magnetic induction takes place through a magnetic substance.

magnetic material. A substance which readily causes magnetism or becomes a magnet. Iron and steel in their different forms are the only important magnetic materials.

magnetic metals. The following metals, in addition to iron, are recognized as magnetic: Nickel, cobalt, chromium, and cerium. With respect to magnetic properties, only cobalt and nickel are comparable with iron. In fact they all are inferior.

magnetic permeability. The specific susceptibility of any mass to magnetization. Magnetic inductive capacity.

magnetic poles. The ends of a magnet, where the attractive force is greatest. In the bar magnet, that end which tends to point north is called the north or positive pole and the other the south or negative pole.

magnetic repulsion. Repulsion reciprocally exerted between like magnet poles.

magnetic retentivity. The resistance offered by a body to any variation of magnetism. The property of iron or other magnetic substance by which it slowly receives and parts with a magnetic condition. Hysteretic retention of magnetism after the magnetizing force has been withdrawn.

magnetic saturation. The state of a magnet which has reached the highest degree of magnetization to which it can attain.

magnetic strength. In a magnetic circuit, the number of lines of force per unit of cross-sectional area.

magnetite. The magnetic oxide of iron. A mineral which is attracted by a magnet and attracts iron; lodestone.

magnetize. To convert a material into a magnet by causing the molecules to rearrange.

magneto. A rotating machine for converting mechanical energy into electrical energy in which the armature rotates in a field produced by permanent magnets instead of electromagnets, as in a dynamo. Formerly magnetos were extensively used for automobile ignition, but have been largely replaced by the storage battery charged by a dynamo operated by the engine.

magnetometer. An instrument for measuring the intensity of magnetic force, especially that of terrestrial magnetism.

magnetron. Microwaves are generated by an electron tube called a magnetron. The tube is capable of generating pules of up to one billion hertz (one gigahertz).

magnet stone. Magnetite, the magnetic ore of iron, a chemical combination of iron with oxygen, possessing the power of attracting iron as a natural magnet; the lodestone.

magnet wire. Single-strand wire with a thin flexible insulation, suitable for winding coils.

magpie cable. A telephone cable containing a double pair of conductors.

main. One of the principal conductors in a power or lighting distribution system. A feeder extending from the service switch, general bus, or converter bus to the main distribution center.

main switchgear connections. Those that electrically connect together devices in the main circuit, or connect them to the bus, or both.

maintained contact. A conventional switch, one that stays in its last set position; one that is not "momentary."

maintenance. Repair service and inspection at prescribed intervals for the upkeep of property or equipment.

main terminal. A termination for the primary winding on rotating machinery.

make. To complete a circuit or to close it.

make and break. To complete and open a circuit alternately.

make contact. The normally open contacts of a relay or pushbutton; the ones that close when the coil is energized and open when de-energized. The opposite of "break" contacts.

malfunction. An error that results from failure in the hardware.

mandrel. In underground cable construction, a metallic cylinder used to insure proper alignment in laying a single duct conduit by being drawn through the duct as each section is laid on.

manhole. In an underground conduit system, a vault built under the street, having a circular opening at the street surface covered by a cast iron cover, and large enough to conveniently admit a man, so that access may be had to the conduit ducts and the cables.

manometer. An instrument, consisting of a U-shaped tube partly filled with mercury, for measuring the pressure of gases.

manual. Operated by mechanical force, applied directly by personal intervention.

manual controller. One having all of its basic functions performed by hand.

manual reset. The manual operation required after safety shutdown before the equipment can be restarted.

manufacturer. A manufacturer or assembler of a product at whose factory a Third Party Certification Program is established.

marine electric apparatus. Electric apparatus designed especially for use on shipboard to withstand the conditions peculiar to such application.

marine junction box. A junction box for electrical connections, of special watertight construction, suitable for use on shipboard.

marquee. A permanent canopy, usually of metal, projecting over an entrance.

mass. Quantity of matter; the physical property that determines the acceleration of a body as the result of an applied force.

master switch. A switch that dominates the operation of contactors, relays, or other remotely operated devices.

mathematics. That science which treats of the exact relations existing between quantities or magnitudes. The science of quantities is afterwards divided into pure and mixed mathematics.

mat switch. A very thin, pressure-sensing switch placed under a carpet or mat to trip an alarm.

matter. Matter is a physical entity that exhibits mass.

maximum. Having the greatest value. A value greater than any which precedes or follows it in succession of values.

maximum continuous rating. The maximum values of electric and mechanical loads at which a machine will operate successfully and continuously.

maximum demand. The greatest of all the demands which have occurred during a given period. It is determined by measurement, according to specifications, over a prescribed time in service.

maximum starting current. The greatest value reached by the starting current of a motor. For squirrel cage induction motors starting currents may be between four and five times the full load current.

maximum system voltage. The highest voltage at which a system is operated.

maximum value. The greatest value reached by AC current or voltage during any point in the cycle.

maximum volts and amperes. In the operation of an alternator the pressure and strength of the current are continually rising, falling, and reversing. During each cycle, there are two points at which the voltage or current reaches its greatest value, being known as the maximum value. This maximum value is not used to any great extent, but it shows the maximum to which the voltage rises, and hence, the greatest strain to which the insulation of the alternator is subjected.

maxwell. The unit of magnetic flux, being the amount of magnetism passing through every square centimeter of a field of unit density, that is, one gauss (one line of force per sq. cm.).

McIntire sleeve joint. A method of joining wires in which a sleeve is used consisting of two copper tubes soldered together, and having bores corresponding to the size of the wires to be joined; the ends of the wires being inserted by a special tool the whole is twisted together, no solder being required.

mean. Average. Having an intermediate value between two extremes.

mean proportional. A number that is both the second and third terms of a proportion. When three numbers are proportional, the second term is called the mean proportional between the other two.

measurand. A physical or electrical quantity, property, or condition that is to be measured.

measure. The number that expresses the ratio of quantity to the unit used in measuring it.

measurement. The determination of the magnitude or amount of a quantity by comparison with the prototype standards of the system of units employed.

mechanical efficiency. The ratio of work done by a machine to the work done on it or energy used by it.

mechanical equivalent of heat. The mechanical energy corresponding to a given quantity of heat energy or the equivalent of mechanical energy in heat which would be necessary to raise the temperature of a unit of mass of water to one degree F.

mechanical latching relay. A relay in which the armature or contacts may be latched mechanically in the operated or unoperated position until reset manually or electrically.

medium lampholder. One with a screw diameter of one inch.

meg or mega. A prefix to a unit of measurement to denote one million times that unit.

mega-volt. A unit of pressure equal to one million volts.

megger. A test instrument used to measure insulation resistance. it is a portable hand operated DC generator used as an ohmmeter.

megger testing set. An instrument for insulation testing and high resistance measurements. It consists essentially of a direct reading true ohmmeter of the permanent magnet, moving coil type mounted in a suitable case, with a hand driven magneto or provided with other means for supplying DC voltage for the test.

megohm. A unit of electrical resistance equal to one million ohms (1,000,000).

mel. A unit of pitch as used in sound.

melting time. The time between the initiation of a current large enough to cause the current-responsive element to melt and the instant when arcing starts.

memory relay. A relay having two or more coils, each of which may operate independent sets of contacts, and another set of contacts that remain in a position determined by the last coil energized.

mensuration. The process of measuring the length of lines, the area of surfaces, and the volume of solids.

mercerized cotton. Cotton which has been chemically treated to resemble silk. Looks like spun silk, but fades more readily.

mercurial contact. An electric contact obtained by means of mercury.

mercurial thermostat. An apparatus for closing an electric circuit by means of a mercurial contact effected by the expansion of mercury when heated.

mercury. One of the metallic chemical elements; also called quick silver. It becomes a fluid at ordinary temperatures; becomes a solid at -38 degrees F. and bolts at 675 degrees F.

mercury relay. A relay in which the movement of mercury opens and closes contacts.

mercury switch. A type of switch which employs mercury as one of the contacts. In operation, the circuit is closed and opened by the other contact dipping into and rising from the mercury.

mercury tilt switch. A switch that is sensitive to position. The switch contains a small globule of mercury, which is a liquid metal and therefore is a conductor. The globule rolls around inside the switch as it is tilted and either makes or breaks the circuit.

mesh. The engagement of one tooth or set of gear teeth with another, as of two spur gears, or of a rack and a pinion.

messenger wire. A steel rope stretched tightly between poles for the purpose of supporting aerial cables which do not have sufficient strength to support their own weight.

metal. An element that forms a base by combining with oxygen. It is usually a good conductor of heat and electricity; generally hard, heavy, malleable, and tenacious. Metals, as known to the ancients were: Gold, silver, copper, iron, tin, and lead.

metal clad. The conducting parts are entirely enclosed in a metal casing.

metal-enclosed bus. An assembly of rigid conductors with associated connections, joints, and insulating supports within a grounded metal enclosure.

metallic circuit. A circuit of which the ground or earth forms no part.

metallic filament. An incandescent lamp filament made of tantalum, tungsten, or other metals. Tungsten is the metal generally used.

metallization. An electrically conductive metal coating on the surface of a cell.

metallurgy. The science which treats of the reduction of metals from their ores.

meter. An electric indicating instrument as a voltmeter, ammeter, etc.

metric system. A method of measurement adopted in France in 1795 and its use was authorized in Great Britain in 1864, and in the United States in 1866. The important feature of the metric system is that it is based upon the decimal scale, therefore, the student should first acquire knowledge of decimals before taking up the metric system.

mho. A unit of conductance being the reciprocal of ohm. It is the conductance of a body having a resistance of one ohm. Note that mho is ohm spelled backwards.

mhometer. An instrument for measuring electrical conductance in terms of the mho.

mica. A mineral substance, distinguished by nearly perfect cleavage, largely used for insulating purposes because of its excellent properties of insulation and durability.

micanite. An insulating material made of mica and shellac.

micro. A prefix to a unit of measurement to denote one-millionth part of that ampere.

microampere. A unit of current equal to one-millionth of an ampere.

micron. The millionth part of a meter.

microvolt. A unit of pressure equal to one-millionth of a volt.

microwaves. A term used rather loosely to signify radio waves in the frequency range from about 1000 megahertz and up.

mil. A unit of length equal to one-thousandth (.001) part of an inch, used especially in the measurement of diameters of wires.

milfoot. A volume of one mil in diameter and one foot long. This unit is used as a basis for computing the resistance of any given wire.

mild steel. A class of steel of great tenacity and ductility which is an alloy of iron with a very small percentage of carbon; it has crystalline structure and is weldable but cannot be hardened. Mild steel is used for the cores of electromagnets.

milli. A prefix meaning one-thousandth (1/1000), such as a millilamp.

milliammeter. An ammeter that measures current in thousandths of an ampere.

minus charge. A negative charge.

mistake. A human action that produces an unintended result.

modulating control. A control in which corrective action is in small increments, as opposed to complete on-off action.

mogul lampholder. One with a screw diameter of 1 1/2 inches.

moisture-resistant. So constructed or treated that it will not be injured readily by exposure to a moist atmosphere.

molecule. The smallest particle of a compound which can maintain the properties of the compound. It consists of a combination of two or more atoms of different kinds.

moment. The product of the force by the shortest distance from the point of rotation to the extension of the line of the force, when a force is applied so as to tend to produce rotation around a point; such distance being the perpendicular to the extension of the line through the point of rotation.

momentary contact switch. A pushbutton or similar type of switch that returns to normal when released. Opposite of maintained contact switch.

momentary current. The current flowing in a device, an assembly, or a bus at the major peak of the maximum cycle.

momentum. The quantity of motion in a moving body, obtained by multiplying the mass of the body by its velocity. Momentum might also be defined as numerically equivalent to the number of pounds of force that will stop a moving body in one second or the number of pounds of force which, acting during one second, will give it a given velocity.

monitored alarm. A local bell alarm that is also monitored at a remote location, usually via telephone lines; a combination local bell alarm and silent alarm.

monolithic conduit. A monolithic concrete structure built to the desired duct formation by an automatic conduit forming machine.

moore light. An early form of vacuum tube lamp. It consists of a long tube in whose ends are fitted carbon electrodes, connected to the outside by platinum wire sealed in glass.

Morse code. A system of dot and dash signals, invented by Samuel Morse, now used to limited extent for wire telegraphy.

motion detector. Any of several devices that detects an intruder by his motion within a protected area.

motor. A device for converting electrical energy into mechanical energy.

motor capacitor. A device designed to improve the starting ability of single-phase induction motors.

motor continuous duty. A motor that, under any normal condition of use, can operate unattended and under load for 3 hours or more.

motor controller. A device or group of devices that serve to govern, in some predetermined manner, the electric power delivered to the motor or group of motors to which it is connected.

motor, directly accessible. A motor that can be contacted without opening or removing any part of an enclosure or guard or is located so as to be accessible to contact.

motorette. A model for endurance tests on samples of rotating machine insulation.

motor-field control. A method of controlling the speed of a motor by means of a change in the magnitude of the field current.

motor-generator. A motor and a generator with a common shaft used to convert line voltages to other voltages or frequencies.

motor, open. A motor having ventilating openings that permit passage of external cooling air over and around the windings of the motor.

motor, totally enclosed. A motor that is enclosed to prevent the free exchange of air between the inside and outside of the enclosure for windings but not sufficiently enclosed to be airtight.

motor torque. The rotary effort which an electric motor develops.

mounting block. A device made of polymeric material intended to mechanically couple ties or straps to a mounting surface.

moving contact assembly. That part of the starting switch assembly on rotating machinery that is actuated by the centrifugal mechanism.

muffler. An attachment for the vent of a fuse, or a vented fuse, that confines the arc and substantially reduces the venting from the fuse.

multiconductor cable. It consists of a number of individually insulated wires, either solid or stranded, which may or may not be grouped together within an outer covering. Sometimes an outer sheath of lead or steel is placed over the cable.

multifamily dwelling. A building containing three or more dwelling units.

multilayer. Consists of alternate layers of conductors and base materials bonded together, including at least one internal conductive layer.

multimeter. A "universal" electrical measuring instrument designed to serve the purposes of a voltmeter, ammeter, ohmeter, and ground detector.

multioutlet assembly. A type of surface or flush raceway designed to hold conductors and receptacles, assembled in the field or at the factory.

multiphase. Containing more than one phase.

multiple. A group of terminals arranged to make a circuit or group of circuits accessible at a number of points, at any one of which connection can be made.

multiple circuit. A method of connection in which current consuming devices are connected across the two leads or mains forming the circuit. Usually called parallel circuit.

multiple feeder. Two or more feeders connected in parallel.

multiple joint. A joint for connecting a branch conductor or cable to a main conductor or cable, to provide a branch circuit.

multiple switch. A switch having contacts for several circuits.

multiplex winding. An armature winding with two or more independent sets of coils. The number of paths in parallel is equal to that of the simplex winding, multiplied by the number of independent windings.

multiple winding. A lap winding as distinguished from a wave winding. Do not confuse with multiplex winding. A multiple winding has as many circuits from negative to positive brushes as there are poles in the machine.

multiplier, instrument. A series resistor connected to a meter mechanism for the purpose of providing a higher voltage indicating range.

multipolar. A machine having more than two magnetic poles; two-pole type is known as bipolar or two pole.

multipolar field. A field generated by several separate magnets.

multirate meter. A meter that registers at different rates or on different dials at different hours of the day.

multiwire branch circuit. A branch circuit consisting of two or more ungrounded conductors having a potential difference between them, and a grounded conductor having equal potential difference between it and each ungrounded conductor of the circuit and which is connected to the neutral conductor of the system.

mutual inductance. The property of a circuit which permits the action of mutual induction; the production of varying or alternating emf in one circuit by movement across its conductors of field lines rising from another nearby circuit with varying current.

myria. A prefix used with a physical unit to designate a unit ten thousand times as great.

myriacycle. Ten kilocycles or 10,000 cycles per second.

N

N. North pole as a magnet.

nameplate. A plaque giving the manufacturer's name and rating of the machine.

n.c. Abbreviation for normally closed contact.

N.E.C. National Electrical Code.

needle. The pointer which swings over the dial of an electric or other measuring instrument.

negative. The opposite of positive. A potential less than that of another potential or of the earth. In electrical apparatus, the pole or direction toward which the current is suppose to flow.

negative charge. The condition in which a body has more than the normal quantities of negative electrons; more negative electricity than an uncharged or neutral body.

negative conductor. A conductor connected to the negative terminal of a source of supply.

negative electrode. The anode when the cell is discharging.

negative plate. The grid and active material to which current flows from the external circuit when the battery is discharging.

negative terminal. The terminal toward which positive electric charge flows in the external circuit from the positive terminal.

negative voltage. A pressure less than that of the earth, the latter being taken as zero.

neon gas. One of the natural gases in the air prevalent in the proportion of one part of neon to every 66,000 parts of air. When neon gas, as in a neon luminous tube light, is excited by passing electric current through it; the gas glows with a characteristic color.

neon-glow lamp tester. A device for determining if a circuit is live, for determining polarity of DC circuits, and for determining if a circuit is AC or DC.

nernst lamp. An incandescent lamp having for its light giving element, a pencil composed of the refractory oxides of rare earth, termed the "glower", which becomes incandescent upon the passage of an electric current. The glower is an insulator when cold, but becomes a conductor when heated.

network. An electric circuit in which the parts are connected in some special manner and cannot be classed as in series, in parallel, or in series-parallel.

neutral. Neither positive nor negative; having zero potential; having electrical potential intermediate between the potentials of other associated parts of the circuit, positive with reference to some parts, negative with reference to others.

neutral bus bar. In the three-wire system of electrical distribution, a bus bar connected to a point between the two dynamos.

neutral conductor. In a three wire system, the middle wire is connected to the lead joining the two electrical sources which are in series. The neutral wire keeps the system balanced in the case of unequal loading, that is, a current will flow through it, to or from the current sources according to the preponderance of load on the one side or the other. The neutral conductor carries the unbalanced current, if the system is balanced the neutral conductor carries zero current. Theoretically, the size of the neutral conductor has to be only sufficient to carry the largest current that will pass through it, which would be the maximum unbalance current.

neutral currents. Stray electric currents which traverse the ground, often escaping from electric railway and other electric systems; earth currents.

neutral feeder load. The feeder neutral load shall be the maximum unbalance of the load. The maximum unbalanced load shall be the maximum net computed load between the neutral and any one ungrounded conductor.

neutral ground. An intentional ground applied to the neutral conductor or neutral point of a circuit, machine, transformer, or system.

neutron. A proton and an electron in very close union existing in the nucleus. A particle having the weight of a proton but carrying no electric charge. It is located in the nucleus of an atom.

newton. The unit of force. The newton is the force that will impart an acceleration of 1 meter per second to a mass of 1 kilogram.

niche. A recess in a wall. A swimming pool has a niche in the wall to install the underwater light.

nichrome. An alloy of nickel, iron, and chromium with high resistance and capable of standing high temperature; used in heating elements.

nickel. A grayish, white, malleable, ductile metal capable of a high polish. It is magnetic but is not easily oxidized, hence its use in nickel plating.

nipple. A piece of pipe not exceeding 24 inches in length threaded at each end. A nipple can be filled 60% conductor fill and Note 8 Ampacity Derating does not apply to a nipple.

nit. The unit of luminance equal to one candela per square meter.

nitrate. A salt formed by the action of nitric acid on a base.

nitrogen lamp. An incandescent lamp in which the filament is placed in a nitrogen filled tube.

n.o. Abbreviation for normally open contact.

no-load. The state of a machine rotating at normal speed under rated conditions, but when no output is required of it.

no load current. A very small current which flows in the primary of a transformer when the secondary is open. The reason for this is as follows: The alternating current flowing in the primary winding causes repeated reversals of magnetic flux through the iron core. These variations of flux induce pressures in both coils; that induced in the primary called the reverse pressure is opposite in direction and very nearly equal to the impressed pressure, that is, to the pressure applied to the primary winding. Accordingly, the only force available to cause current to flow through the primary winding is the difference between the impressed pressure and reverse pressure, this difference being called the effective pressure.

no-load test. A test in which the machine is run as a motor providing no useful mechanical output from the shaft.

nominal system voltage. A nominal value assigned to designate a system of a given voltage class.

non-arcing fuse. A fuse wire which, by reason of being made of non-arcing metal, or encased in an air-tight tube, blows without forming a voltaic arc.

nonautomatic. Action requiring personal intervention for its control. As applied to an electric controller, nonautomatic control does not necessarily imply a manual controller, but only that personal intervention is necessary.

nonbearing wall. Wall that carries no load other than its own weight.

noncoincident demand. The sum of the individual maximum demands regardless of time of occurrence within a specified period.

nonconductor. An insulating material; one which offers extreme opposition to the flow of electricity.

nonferric. Without iron.

nonferrous metals. Those not obtained from iron.

noninductive circuit. A circuit having no inductance, or one in which the inductance is neutralized by capacity. In a noninductive circuit the current is in phase with the voltage, unless the capacity be more than enough to neutralize the inductance. When this condition occurs the current leads the voltage.

nonmagnetic. A property of any substance which cannot be magnetized. There are many nonmagnetic materials such as paper, glass, wood, etc. which are not affected by magnetic fields.

nonmagnetic steel. Certain grades of nickel, steel, and other steel alloys which can be practically unmagnetizable. Aluminum is a nonmagnetic alloy.

nonmetallic-sheathed cable. Nonmetallic-sheathed cable is a factory assembly of two or more insulated conductors having an outer sheath of moisture-resistant, flame-retardant, nonmetallic material. Often referred to as Romex.

nonmetallic surface extension. Two individually insulated conductors attached to a fabric or other device arranged for convenient fastening to walls or other exposed surfaces.

nonmetallic waterproof wiring. A multiple-conductor, rubber sheathed cable used for exposed wiring in wet locations where exposed to mild corrosive fumes or vapors.

nonrenewable cartridge fuse. A fuse in which the fusible element is encased in a fibre tube filled with noninflammible material and closed at the end with ferrules. On arcing, part of the fusible element is vaporized, and the filling compound absorbs or chills and condenses this vapor, rendering it nonconducting and thereby extinguishing the arc.

nonreversing. A control function that provides for operation in one direction only.

nonstop switch. A switch that, when operated, will prevent the elevator from making registered landing stops.

nonvented fuse. A fuse without intentional provision for the escape of arc gases, liquids, or solid particles to the atmosphere during circuit interruption.

nonventilated enclosure. An enclosure designed to provide limited protection against the entrance of dust, dirt, or other foreign objects.

normal. A line perpendicular to a plane. Consonant with rule. Regular.

normal current. The force of current at which a system is intended to work.

normal frequency. The frequency at which a device or system is designed to operate.

normally closed (n.c.) and normally open (n.o.). The terms normally closed and normally open, when applied to a magnetically operated switching device, such as a contactor or relay, or to the contacts thereof, signify the position taken when the operating magnet is de-energized. These terms apply only to nonlatching type of devices.

normal operation. Intrinsically safe apparatus or associated apparatus conforming electrically and mechanically with its design specifications.

181

normal operating conditions. Any operating conditions of the device, including overload up to 400 percent (circuit breakers, switches, and the like) and a stalled rotor condition for any motor with the circuit protected by an overcurrent protective device specified by the product manufacturer.

normal position. A predetermined position that serves as a starting point for all operations.

normal standby condition. The ready-to-operate condition existing prior to tripping or operation of the product.

north pole of magnet. The pole of a magnet, or magnetic needle, which tends to point to the north; also known as the boreal, marked, north seeking, positive, plus (+), and red pole.

notching. A qualifying term applied to any relay indicating that a number of separate impulses are required to complete its operation.

notching relay. A programming relay in which the response is dependent upon successive impulses of the input quantity.

no voltage release. A switch held by an electromagnet in a closed position and released when voltage across the magnet windings drops to a predetermined minimum.

nucleus. The central part of an atom that is mainly comprised of protons and neutrons. It is the part of the atom that has the most mass.

null. Zero.

numerator. That part of a fraction which expresses the number of parts taken.

O

oblique angle. Any angle except 0, 90, 180, 270, or 360 degrees.

oblong. Descriptive of a rectangle that is not extremely elongated. Having one principal axis longer than the other, or others.

observable temperature. The temperature of equipment obtained on test or in operation.

observable temperature rise. The difference between observable temperature and the ambient temperature at the time of test.

obtuse angle. One greater than a right angle. (90 degrees)

occulting light. A rhythmic light in which the periods of light are clearly longer than the periods of darkness.

oersted. The unit of reluctance or magnetic resistance, being the reluctance offered by a cube centimeter of vacuum.

off-peak power. Power supplied during designated periods of relatively low system demands.

off period. The part of an operating cycle during which essentially no current flows in the circuit switching element.

offset fitting. A pipe fitting for joining two parallel pipe lines. In piping sometimes part of a pipe line must be in a position parallel with, but not in alignment with the balance of the pipe.

ohm. The unit of electrical resistance. Resistance is one ohm when a DC voltage of one volt will send a current of one ampere through.

ohmic contact. A purely resistive contact.

ohmic resistance test. A test to measure the ohmic resistance of a winding, using direct current.

ohmmeter. A form of galvanometer for measuring electrical resistance in which a pointer indicates directly the number of ohms in the resistance under measurement.

Ohm's law. The relationship between voltage, current, and resistance in a DC circuit or the relationship between voltage, current, and impedance in AC circuits.

oil. The prefix oil, applied to a device that interrupts an electric circuit, indicates that the interruption occurs in oil.

oil circuit breaker. A type of switch in which the circuit is broken under oil. Specially adapted for high voltage AC circuits of large power. The oil breaker terminates the AC wave at its normal zero value, eliminating excessive surges in the connected circuits and reduces fire and life hazards.

oil cooled transformer. A type in which the coils and core are immersed in oil and provided with ducts to allow the oil to circulate by convection and thus serve as a medium to transmit the heat to the case, from which it passes by radiation. The oil, heated by contact with the exposed surfaces of the core and coils, rises to the surface, flows outward and descends along the sides of the transformer case from the outer surface of which the heat is radiated into the air.

oil-filled cable. A self-contained pressure cable in which the pressure medium is low-viscosity oil having access to the insulation.

oilproof enclosure. An enclosure so constructed that oil vapors, or free oil not under pressure, which may accumulate within the enclosure, will not prevent successful operation of, or cause damage to, the enclosed equipment.

oil seal. A part or combination of parts in a bearing assembly intended to prevent leakage of oil from the bearing.

184

oil slinger. A rotating member mounted on the shaft of rotating machinery that expels oil by centrifugal force and tends to prevent it from creeping along the surface.

okonite. A compound of high resistance employed for insulation purposes.

omnibus bars. Commonly called bus bars, the main switchboard conductors to which the current is led from a dynamo or alternator through suitable cables, switches, and indicating instruments.

ondometer. A name sometimes used for a frequency meter.

one-family dwelling. A building consisting solely of one dwelling unit.

one-line diagram. A diagram that shows, by means of single lines and graphic symbols, the course of an electric circuit or system of circuits and the component devices or parts used therein.

opaline. Trade name for a translucent glass designed to soften and diffuse the light of an electric lamp.

open circuit. A circuit, the electrical continuity of which has been interrupted, as by opening a switch.

open-circuit control. A method of controlling motors employing the open-circuit method of transition from series to parallel connections of motors.

open-circuit transition. A method of starting in which the power to the motor is interrupted during normal starting sequence.

open-circuit voltage. The voltage at the terminals when no appreciable current is flowing.

open delta connection. A method of connecting two transformers so that they form only two sides of a delta or triangular connection, in place of the three sides with three transformers in a regular delta connection. Open delta operates at 57.7% power of a regular delta connection.

opening, handhole size. An opening 4 inches in diameter or larger, or an opening through which a 4 inch diameter sphere will pass.

opening, manhole size. An opening with a clear cross section area of 96 square inches or more, and with the smallest dimension exceeding 6 inches.

opening time. The time interval between the time when the actuating quantity of the release circuit reaches the operating value and the instant when the primary arcing contacts have parted.

open loop. A signal path without feedback.

open-loop series lighting system. A street lighting system in which the circuits each consist of a single line wire that is connected from lamp to lamp and returned by a separate route to the source of supply.

open machine. One of either the pedestal bearing or end bracket type, with no restriction to ventilation, other than that imposed by good mechanical construction.

open-phase protection. A form of protection that operates to disconnect the protected equipment on the loss of current in one phase conductor of a polyphase circuit.

open wiring. Insulated wires supported on knobs, cleats, or other insulators, but without any other enclosure or covering, not concealed by the building structure.

operating temperature. The range of environmental temperatures in which a power supply can safely be operated.

operating voltage. The voltage of the system on which a device is operated. AC voltage is usually expressed as a rms value.

operator. The person using or operating the equipment.

opposite phase. A 180 degree phase difference.

opposite polarity. A difference of potential between two points, where shorting of these two points would result in a condition involving overload, rupting of printed wiring-board tracks, components or fuses, and the like.

opposition. The relation between two periodic functions when the phase difference between them is 1/2 of a period.

orangeburg. A nonmetallic pipe used for underground installations by plumbers.

orifice, heating equipment. The opening in a cap, spud, or other device, whereby the flow of gas is limited and through which the gas is discharged to a burner.

oscillating. Alternately surging first in one direction and then in the reverse direction.

oscillating circuit. A reactive circuit in which induction and capacity are in such proportion that an oscillating current can be set up.

oscillating current. An electric current which alternately reverses its direction in a circuit in a periodic manner; the frequency being dependent solely on the constants of the system.

oscillation. The variation, usually with time, of the magnitude of a quantity with respect to a specified reference when the magnitude is alternately greater and smaller than the reference.

oscillator. An apparatus intended to produce electric or mechanical oscillations.

187

oscilloscope. An instrument primarily for making visible the instantaneous values of one or more rapidly varying electrical quantities as a function of time or of another electrical quantity.

osmium. A rare metal employed as a filament in a certain type of incandescent lamp. It is nearly twice as heavy as lead and is almost infusible. It is malleable and ductile with high electric resistance. The pure metal is not drawn into fine wire for filaments, but finely divided osmium is mixed into a paste which is forced through dies, producing threads which are formed by heating by an electric current in the presence of certain gases.

osmose, electric. When two liquids are separated by a porous diaphragm and a strong current of electricity is passed through from the liquid on the one side through the diaphragm, to the liquid on the other side, the liquid on the side to which the current is passing rises in level.

outage. The state of component when it is not available to perform its intended function due to some event directly associated with that component.

outdoor. Designed for use outside buildings.

outdoor location. In the open and subjected to the full effects of weathering.

outdoor transformer. A transformer with weatherproof construction.

outlet. A point on the wiring system at which current is taken to supply utilization equipment.

outlet box. A box used on a wiring system, usually at an outlet. It is provided with means for connection to a wiring system and intended primarily to enclose splices and wiring devices, but may be also acceptable as the support of a fixture or other equipment intended for similar installation. This box may or may not be provided with studs or a bar hanger or with clamps for securing cable, tubing, or conduit.

outlet box, concrete type. A box intended for support in concrete. It may be constructed to permit end-to-end extension and the application of covers on two sides. It is not intended for installation in a floor.

outlet box, floor type. A box provided with means for flush mounting in a floor. It is sealed against the entrance of scrub water at floor level.

outlet box, flush-device type. A box provided with ears or flanges with threaded holes spaced to accept the mounting yoke of a wiring device or devices. This box is provided with a mounting means, and it may or may not include clamps for connection of cable, tubing, or conduit.

outlet lighting. An arrangement of incandescent lamps or electric discharge tubing to outline or call attention to certain features, such as the shape of a building or the decoration of a window.

outlet receptacle. An outlet used with one or more receptacles that are not of the screw-shell type.

out of phase. Phase difference, as between current and pressure in an alternating current, the phase difference being measured by the angle. When the phase difference is 90 degrees, the two alternating quantities are said to be in quadrature; when it is 180 degrees, they are said to be in opposition. When they are in quadrature, one is at a maximum when the other is at zero. When they are in opposition, one reaches a positive maximum when the other reaches a negative maximum, being at each instant opposite in sign.

out of step. A system condition in which two or more synchronous machines have lost synchronism with each other and are operating at different average frequencies.

output. The current, voltage, power, or driving force delivered by a circuit or device.

output of dynamo. The available electrical power delivered by a dynamo at its terminals, measured in watts or kilowatts. The volts and amperes from which the watts are calculated being measured at the terminals of the machine; the net output being the number of amperes multiplied by the volts at the terminals.

output of motor. The mechanical power delivered to the pulley of a motor measured as brake horsepower.

output winding (secondary winding). The winding(s) from which the output is obtained.

outside wiring. Wiring that is attached to the surface; not concealed.

oven, wall-mounted. An oven for cooking purposes designed for mounting in or on a wall or other surface and consisting of one or more heating elements, internal wiring, and built-in or separately mountable controls.

over-all electrical efficiency. The ratio of the power absorbed by the load material to the total power drawn from the supply lines.

overcurrent. Any current in excess of the rated current of the equipment or the ampacity of a conductor. It may result from overload, short-circuit, or ground fault.

overcurrent protection. A form of protection (fuse or circuit breaker)that operates when the current exceeds a predetermined value.

overcurrent relay. A relay that operates when the current through the relay during its operating period is equal to or greater than its setting.

overhead conductor. A conductor suspended overhead, as distinguished from one placed underground; an aerial conductor.

overload. Operation of equipment in excess of normal, full load rating, or of a conductor in excess of rated ampacity which, when it persists for a sufficient length of time, would cause damage or dangerous overheating. A fault, such as a short-circuit or ground fault, it is not an overload.

overload capacity. The current, voltage, or power level beyond which permanent damage occurs to the device considered. This is usually higher than the rated load capacity.

overload protection. Overload protection is the effect of a device operative on excessive current, but not necessarily on short-circuit, to cause and maintain the interruption of current flow to the device governed.

overload relay (heater). One which functions at a predetermined value or current to cause the disconnection of the motor from the line.

overspeed limit device. A device which functions on machine overspeed.

overvoltage. A voltage above the normal rated voltage or the maximum operating voltage of a device or circuit. A direct test of overvoltage is a voltage above the peak of the line alternating voltage.

oxidation. Loss of electrons by a constituent of a chemical reaction.

oyster fitting. A fitting used for incandescent lamps in watertight compartments on ships.

ozone. A compound consisting of three atoms of oxygen, produced by the action of electric sparks, or specialized electrical devices.

ozonizer. An apparatus employing electric discharges to produce ozone.

P

P. Abbreviation for power.

pace voltage. A voltage generated by ground current between two points on the surface of the ground, at a distance apart corresponding to the conventional length of an ordinary pace.

packing gland. An explosionproof entrance for conductors through the wall of an explosionproof enclosure.

pair. Two. Usually, two wires such as a pair of telephone wires.

paired cable. A cable in which all of the conductors are arranged in the form of twisted pairs, none of which is arranged with others to form quads.

palm rule. If the palm of the right hand be held facing or against the lines of force, and the thumb in the direction of the motion, then the fingers will point in the direction of the induced current. In electromagnetic induction, a rule for direction of induced current.

pancake coil. A flat coil of wire adjusted to the surface of an armature.

panelboard. A single panel or group of panel units designed for assembly in the form of a single panel; including buses, automatic overcurrent devices, and with or without switches for the control of light, heat, or power circuits; designed to be placed in a cabinet or cutout box placed in or against a wall or partition and accessible only from the front.

panel feeder. A feeder leading to a bus bar connected with a panel.

panic alarm. A local bell alarm, triggered manually, usually by pushing a button.

paper cable. An electric cable insulated by wrappings of specially prepared paper.

paper condenser. A condenser having a dielectric composed of paper. A better condenser would be of mica.

paraffin. A colorless or white, waxy substance obtained by dry distillation from wood, coal, peat, petroleum, etc. largely used in electrical work for its moistureproof and insulating properties.

paraffined wire. An insulated electric wire provided with a final coating of paraffin.

parallel connected transformers. Transformers in a system of electric distribution having all their primary coils connected across the mains in parallel. In paralleling transformers, it is essential that the terminals have the same polarity at a given instant, and the transformers should have practically identical characteristics.

parallel connection. A method of connecting up an electric system in which all the positive poles, or terminals, are joined to one conductor, and all the negative poles to the other; multiple connection.

parallel feeder. One that operates in parallel with one or more feeders of the same type from the same source.

parallelogram. A quadrilateral which has its opposite sides parallel.

parallel winding. A method of armature winding, usually known as lap winding, in which adjacent coils are connected in series instead of the connections progressing in a "wave" around and around the core. Lap winding is characterized by having as many circuits through the armature from positive to negative brushes, as the machine has poles; the current dividing equally between these parallel circuits.

paramagnet. A paramagnetic substance; a substance such as iron, which readily becomes a magnet.

193

paramagnetic. A term introduced by Faraday to denote a substance which acted like iron in regard to a magnetic field; a substance more susceptible to magnetism than air. Paramagnetic substances concentrate the lines of force on them. The most powerful paramagnetic bodies are iron, nickel, and cobalt.

parameter. A variable that is given a constant value for a specific purpose or process.

para rubber. The best grade of India rubber for electrical purposes and the grade generally specified for insulation work.

partial contact. A contact between two electric circuits such as to produce a partial fault in the circuits. Distinguish between partial and intermittent contact.

partial fault. Any fault in an electic circuit which interferes with the proper working of the circuit without causing its complete interruption.

parting. The selective corrosion of one or more components of a solid solution alloy.

partition. An interior wall dividing a room, area of a building, or an enclosure that separates areas.

part-winding starter. A starter that applies voltage successively to the partial sections of the primary winding of an AC motor.

party wall. A common wall between two stores or premises. Typically, in a shopping center, party walls are only plaster or drywall.

passivity. The condition of a surface that retards a specified chemical reaction at that surface.

patch. To connect circuits together temporarily by means of a cord, known as a patch cord.

paying out. Passing out submarine cable while it is being laid from a ship.

P.B.X. An abbreviation for private branch exchange in telephony.

peak. The maximum instantaneous value of a varying voltage or current.

peak current. The maximum value of an alternating current.

peak load. In a power station, the maximum load which has to be carried by the station at any time of day or night, as shown by the highest point of the load curve.

peak-to-peak value. The value of an AC waveform from its positive peak to its negative peak. In the case of a sine wave, the peak-to-peak value is double the peak value.

peak voltage. The maximum value of an alternating voltage.

pear push. A push contact resembling a pear in shape and attached to the end of a pendant flexible cord.

pedestal. That part of the structure above the base that supports the component units, and to which they are attached.

peg switch. A switch that is operated by the insertion or withdrawal of a peg; also called a pin switch.

Peltier effect. A current flowing across the junction of two dissimilar metals, causing either an absorption or liberation of heat, depending on the direction of the current, at a rate proportional to the first power of the current.

penciling. In cable jointing, the insulation around each conductor should be "penciled" back. This is done much in the same manner as sharpening a lead pencil. It is important that the penciling be smooth and even.

195

pendant. An equipment that is suspended from overhead either by means of a flexible cord carrying the current or otherwise.

pendant cord. A flexible cord containing a pair of insulated conductors, employed for suspending incandescent lamps, or for making electrical connection with other movable electric devices.

pendant-type track. A ceiling-mounted track system in which the track sections and connectors are suspended from the ceiling by a metal stem, metal chain, or metal cable.

percentage. The rate per hundred; from the Latin per centum meaning by the hundred, that is a certain part of every hundred.

perforated armature. An armature having a perforated core to admit ventilation.

perimeter. The length of the boundary line of any plane figure.

period. The time required for a complete cycle of alternating current or voltage; for 60 cycles per second, a period would be 1/60 second.

periodic current. A current with periodically varying strength or direction. A current alternating periodically.

periodic duty. Intermittent operation in which the load conditions are regularly recurrent.

permalloy. An alloy of nickel and iron having an abnormally high magnetic permeability.

permanently wired unit. A unit provided with wiring terminals or leads for the connection of power supply conductors. A permanently wired unit has provision for connection of one of the wiring systems in accordance with the National Electrical Code.

196

permanent magnet. A magnet consisting of hard steel which possesses coercive force, or retentivity in a high degree, and is therefore said to retain its magnetism permanently; used in the construction of magnetos.

permeability. The ratio between the number of lines of force per unit area passing through a magnetizable substance, and the magnetizing force which produces them. In other words, it is the ratio of flux density to magnetizing force.

permeameter. An apparatus for determining corresponding values of magnetizing force and flux density in a test specimen.

petticoat insulator. An insulator having at its lower end a deep groove resembling a petticoat. A single cup telephone or telegraph insulator.

p.f. The abbreviation for power factor.

phase. (a) The angle turned through by a generating element of an alternator reckoned from a given instant. Phase is usually measured in degrees from the initial position of zero generation. (b) Any position of an AC of pressure curve as indicated by some reference position. Usually the phase position is defined by specifying the number of electrical degrees between the phase and the reference position.

phase conductor. The conductors other than the neutral conductor.

phase difference. The time in electrical degrees by which one wave leads or lags another.

phase failure protection. The effect of a device operative upon the failure of power in one wire of a polyphase circuit; to cause and maintain the interruption of power in all of the circuit.

phase indicator. An instrument intended for "phasing out", particularly in making relay connections or other connections where a current of a specific phase should be selected in regard to a particular voltage connection.

phase lag. In an AC circuit, when the current reaches a maximum or zero value at a time later than the corresponding values of the pressure, the current is said to be out of phase with the pressure and to lag behind the pressure.

phase lead. In an AC circuit, when the current reaches a maximum or zero value at a time earlier than the corresponding values of the pressure, the current is said to be out of phase with the pressure and to lead the pressure.

phase meter. A synchronism indicator.

phase splitter. A device that produces from a single input wave, two or more output waves that differ in phase from one another.

Phillips screw. A screw having an indented cross in its head in place of the slot.

phon. The unit of loudness level as specified in the definition of loudness level.

phosphor. A substance capable of luminescence.

phosphorescence. The emission of light as the result of the absorption of radiation, and continuing for a noticeable length of time after excitation has been removed.

photoconductive cell. A photocell in which the photoconductive effect is utilized.

photoelectric. Descriptive of the effect which light has on electric circuits, through a device controlled by light.

photoelectric cell. A device which varies in electrical resistance in proportion to the amount of light falling upon it.

photoelectric control. Control by means of which a change in incident light affects a control function.

physiological effect. A current of electricity passed through the body produces muscular contractions which are due to the physiological effects of current.

pickup, relay. The action of a relay as it makes a designated response to increase of input.

pickup voltage or current. The voltage or current at which a magnetic contactor starts to close under conditions of normal operating temperature.

piezoelectric effect. Some materials become electrically polarized when they are mechanically strained.

piezoelectricity. Electricity produced by pressure, such as the electric polarity sometimes seen in a crystalline substance.

piezometer. An instrument for measuring flowing water. If a vertical or oblique tube is inserted into a pipe containing water under pressure, the water will rise in the former, and the vertical height which it reaches will be the head producing the pressure at the point where the tube is attached.

pigtail. A flexible connection between a stationary terminal and a part which has a short range of motion.

pilaster. Flat square column attached to a wall and projecting about a fifth of its width from the face of the wall.

pilot duty. An application involving the control of an electromagnet.

pilot lamp. A lamp that indicates the condition of an associated circuit.

pilot light. A light, associated with a control, that by means of position or color indicates the functioning of the control.

pilot motor. A small motor designed to start and control a large motor.

pin plug. A slender metal plug designed to make an electrical connection when inserted between two contact blocks.

pipe cable. A pressure cable in which the container for the pressure medium is a loose-fitting rigid metal pipe.

pit. A depressed area in a foundation under a machine.

pitting. Localized corrosion taking the form of cavities at the surface.

plain conductor. A conductor consisting of one metal only.

plant electricity. Electricity exhibited in vegetable life; such as differences of voltage existing in various parts of a tree.

plating. The process of covering an object with a coating of metal, as in electroplating.

platinoid. An alloy of copper, zinc, nickel, and tungsten, having a temperature coefficient less than half that of German silver, often employed for resistance wires in resistance boxes. The addition of tungsten imparts greater density, and when polished the alloy has the appearance of silver.

platinum. A somewhat rare, silvery white metal, specific gravity 21.5 nearly the heaviest known, while it melts at about 3190 degrees F. Platinum is very ductile, is not dissolved by any acid and is very difficult to oxidize.

plenum. Chamber or space forming a part of an air-conditioning system.

plug. A device, usually associated with a cord, that by insertion in a jack or receptacle establishes connection between a conductor or conductors associated with the plug and a conductor or conductors connected to the jack or receptacle.

plug adapter. A device that, by insertion in a lampholder, serves as a receptacle.

plug fuse. An enclosed fuse with screw connections. It consists of a cylindrical porcelain body, in which the fuse strip is placed.

plugging. A control function that provides braking by reversing the motor line voltage polarity or phase sequence so that the motor develops a counter-torque that exerts a retarding force.

plug-in device. A device provided with integral blades for direct insertion into a receptacle.

plugmold. A surface raceway used primarily for multioutlet assemblies.

plug, open-circuit. A device similar in construction to a shorting plug, but intended to maintain a lighting fixture in the off mode of operation until removed.

plug, shorting. A plug-in, locking type device, having the same standard 3-blade plug configuration as a control unit and which provides an electrical connection through the control receptacle of an outdoor electric lighting fixture, without performing a control function. A shorting plug is used as a substitute, where necessary, for a control unit and maintains a lighting fixture in the "on" mode of operation until removed.

plumbago. Graphite or "blacklead"; used for crucibles and lubricating and also to coat insulating surfaces as gutta-percha. It is the composition with which the interior of pencils are filled.

plunger. A solid cylindrical body which fits accurately or approximately the chamber within which it reciprocates. It differs from a piston in that it is longer than its stroke.

plunger relay. A relay operated by a movable core or plunger through solenoid action.

pneumatic. Relating to, or using of air, wind, or other gas.

pneumatics. A branch of mechanics that deals with the mechanical properties of gases.

polarity. (a) As applied to electric circuits, it indicates which terminal is positive and which is negative. (b) As applied to magnets, it indicates which pole is N and which is S.

polarity in a circuit. The quality of having two opposite charges, one positive, one negative.

polarization, battery. Polarization is caused by development of gas at the battery electrodes during current demand and has the effect of increasing the internal resistance of the battery.

pole. (a) One end of a magnet, one electrode of a battery. (b) An outdoor support of metal, wood, or the like, over 12 feet tall, on which at least one lighting fixture is intended to be mounted by means of arms or fittings. The height of the support is measured from ground level.

pole climbers. A device consisting of spurs properly supported and braced for attachment to a lineman's shoes to assist him in climbing a pole supporting telephone or other electric wires.

pole guy. A rod, wire, or other appliance for stiffening a pole.

pole line. A series of poles arranged to support conductors above the surface of the ground.

pole strength, magnet. A magnet's pole strength can be estimated by measuring the force with which it attracts or repels another pole, the force being equal to the product of the two polar strengths.

polyphase. Having two or more alternating currents and potentials acting at the same time; more than one phase.

polyphase machine. A machine that generates or utilizes polyphase AC power. These are usually three-phase machines with three voltages displaced 120 electrical degrees with respect to each other.

polyphase motor. A motor which operates from a supply system of more than one phase.

polyvinylchloride. A combination of resin or plastic with a chlorine compound. Known to the electrician as PVC, a conduit or box of insulated material.

pony insulator. A small variety of glass insulator.

porcelain. A hard, opaque solid, manufactured from kaolin mixed with quartz and with a fusible silicate. It has a high insulating strength and resists the entrance of moisture or water. It has the objection of being brittle; heat is liable to break a single long piece of porcelain.

porcelain insulator. An insulator made of glazed porcelains, instead of glass.

portable lighting. Lighting involving lighting equipment designed for manual portability.

portland cement. A calcined compound of chalk and clay, subsequently ground to a fine powder. It possesses the valuable property of hardening under water. In 1886 just north of *Bellefontaine, Ohio*, large marl pits of almost pure calcium carbonate underlaid by blue clay containing silica were found, thus leading to the first concrete street being poured in 1891 beside the courthouse in *Bellefontaine, Ohio*.

positive. The term used to describe a terminal with fewer electrons than normal so that it attracts electrons. Electrons flow into the positive terminals of a voltage source.

positive charge. The electrical condition of a body which has less than the normal quantity of negative electrons.

positive conductor. A conductor connected to the positive terminal of a source of supply.

positive pole. The north seeking or plus (+) pole of a magnet.

positive rotation. Left-handed or counter-clockwise rotation. A rotary motion in a direction opposite to the movement of the hands of a clock as seen when one reads time. A right to left rotation.

post. An outdoor support of metal, wood, or the like, no more than 12 feet tall, on which a lighting fixture is intended to be mounted. The height of the support is as measured from ground level.

potential. Electrical pressure which determines the flow of current through a given resistance or impedance. The term pressure or voltage should be used rather than potential.

potential gradient. The rate of change of potential with respect to the distance between two points.

potential relay. A relay used to start motors requiring a high starting torque. The relay coil is energized by a voltage generated in the starting winding of the motor.

potential transfer. An instrument transformer with its primary connected between opposite sides of a line or between points having a potential difference, and with its secondary connected to a meter or other device which is actuated by the potential difference of the line.

potentiometer. A device for measuring the pressure difference by either totally or partly balancing the unknown against a variable pressure difference, the value of which is known by reference to a voltage standard. There are numerous types of potentiometers, some adapted to high resistance measurements, others for low resistance.

pothead. A device that seals the end of a cable and provides insulated exits for the conductor or conductors.

pothead terminal. In underground construction a method of terminating the lead armor. The pothead is soldered to the lead covering and is filled with pitch. The pothead serves to localize stray currents that might prove disastrous to the cable, and by thoroughly grounding the lead covering, these stray currents are effectively dissipated.

power. The rate at which work is done; it is usually expressed as the number of foot pounds in one minute, that is, if you lift 33,000 foot pounds in one minute, you have done 1 horsepower of work.

power, apparent. The product of the root-mean-square current and the root-mean-square voltage.

power factor. The ratio of the voltage and current, or volt-amperes, that do useful work in an AC circuit or equipment, to the total voltage and current, volt-amperes, flowing in the circuit.

power-factor angle. The angle whose cosine is the power factor.

power factor corrections. The addition of capacitance to alternating current circuit, containing a great deal of inductance, to lessen the amount of current that does no useful work; or, inductance might be added to a circuit containing excessive capacitance.

power factor meter. A meter which indicates the phase relationship between pressure and current, and is therefore sometimes called a phase indicator.

power level. The amount of electrical power passing through a given point in a circuit; may be expressed in watts, decibels, or volume units.

power outlet. An enclosed assembly which may include receptacles, circuit breakers, fuseholders, fused switches, buses, and watt-hour meter mounting means; intended to supply and control power to mobile homes, recreational vehicles, or boats; or to serve as a means for distributing power required to operate mobile or temporarily installed equipment.

power pack. Generally a separate unit connected between the track and the adaptor of the fixture assembly. It is provided with a switching power supply, linear power supply, or isolating transformer to supply power to a track lighting fixture.

power supply. A product intended to convert AC to DC that has a minimum fluctuation in its unidirectional flow. A power supply is intended to provide all of the electrical operating power required by the equipment to which it is connected, when the equipment is operating in its intended manner.

power transmission. When the electric current has to be transmitted along distances for either lighting or power purposes, economy is attainable only by reducing the weight of the copper conductors. This can be accomplished only by the use of the high voltage currents obtainable from alternators.

precast concrete. Concrete units (such as piles or vaults) cast away from the construction site and set in place.

preheat-starting, flourescent lamps. The designation given to those systems in which hot-cathode electric discharge lamps are started from preheated cathodes through the use of a starting switch, either manual or automatic in its operation.

premises. Stores, banks, lofts, warehouses, and the like, used for the storage, manufacturing, sale, or handling of merchandise, valuables, and the like.

premises wiring (system). That interior and exterior wiring, including power, lighting, control, and signal circuit wiring together with all of its associated hardware, fittings, and wiring devices, both permanently and temporarily installed, which extends from the load end of the service drop, or load end of the service lateral conductors to the outlet(s). Such wiring does not include wiring internal to appliances, fixtures, motors, controllers, motor control centers, and similar equipment.

pressel. A push button contact set in a pear shaped handle at the end of a flexible cord, for conveniently ringing a bell or lighting an electric lamp.

presspahn. A name sometimes given to a Fullerboard; a useful material for insulating armature slots. It is mechanically tough and has high disruptive strength.

pressure cable. An oil-impregnated, paper-insulated cable in which positive gauge pressure is maintained on the insulation under all operating conditions.

pressure, electric. Voltage. The words pressure or voltage should always be used instead of expressions such as electromotive force or difference of potential.

pressure switch. A switch in which actuation of the contacts is affected at a predetermined liquid or gas pressure.

pressure wire connector. A device that establishes the connection between two or more conductors and a terminal by means of mechanical pressure and without the use of solder.

primary. The part of a motor or transformer having windings that are connected to the power supply line.

primary and secondary windings. Terms used to distinguish transformer windings in regard to energy flow, the primary being that which receives the energy from the supply circuit and the secondary that which receives the energy by electromagnetic induction from the primary.

primary cell. A device for producing an electric current chemically. The incorrect use of the word battery for cell should be avoided. A primary cell consists of two elements of dissimilar metals placed in an electrolyte or exciting fluid contained in a jar.

primary current. The current in the primary of a transformer.

primary winding. The coil through which current from the source flows to a transformer. In a lighting transformer the primary coil receives high tension current; in an ignition transformer, low tension current.

prime mover. An apparatus or mechanism whereby motion and force are received directly from some natural source of energy, and transmitted into some form of motion by means of which the power may be conveniently applied.

printed circuit. A pattern comprising printed wiring formed in a predetermined design in, or attached to, the surface or surfaces of a common base.

printed-wiring board. A completely processed combination of a printed-wiring pattern, including printed components, and the base material.

prism. A transparent body with, usually, three rectangular plane faces or sides, and two equal and parallel triangular ends or bases; used in experiments on refraction, dispersion, etc.

private residence. A separate dwelling or a separate apartment in a multiple dwelling that is occupied only by the members of a single family unit.

probe. An instrument used to determine accessibility of a live part.

prony brake. A device for making brake horsepower tests. It consists of a friction band which may be placed around the fly wheel or a pulley fixed on the crank shaft, and attached to a lever bearing upon the platform of a weighing scale.

proof test. A fail or no-fail test of the insulation system of a rotating machine made to demonstrate whether the electrical strength of the insulation is above a predetermined maximum value.

proper fraction. One whose numerator is less than its denominator.

proportion. An equality of ratios, that is, when two ratios are equal, the four terms form a proportion.

proportional, directly. Directly proportional means that one factor will be increased in proportion to an increase in another factor.

proportional, inversely. Inversely proportional means that one factor will be increased in proportion to a decrease in another factor or vice versa.

proscenium lighting. The stage lighting in front of a curtain in a theater.

protected location. An area that is partially protected from the effects of weathering through the use of a roof, canopy, marquee, or the like.

protective lighting. A system intended to facilitate the nighttime policing of industrial and other properties.

protective relay. A type used to protect circuits from abnormal conditions of voltage, or current, which would be undesirable or dangerous to the circuit and apparatus contained therein. They act in combination with automatic circuit breakers, operating when their predetermined setting has been reached, energizing the trip coil of the circuit breaker and opening the circuit.

protective signaling. Comprises the initiation, reception, and transmission of signals involved in the detection and prevention of property loss or damage due to fire, burglary, etc.

protectorelay. A device used on oil burners to provide safety ignition of the oil on start-up. It is a heat-sensing control mounted on the unit stack to sense heat coming from the flame. If no heat is detected, the protectorelay will shut the unit down.

proton. The smallest quantity of electricity which can exist in the free state. A positive charged particle in the nucleus of an atom.

proximity switch. A device that reacts to the proximity of an actuating means without physical contact or connection therewith.

pull. An electric contact maker which closes a circuit by a pull; sometimes used in place of a push button; a pull contact.

pull box. A box with a blank cover for insertion into a conduit run, raceway, or tubing, which facilitates the drawing of conductors.

pulsating current. A current which changes in value but not in direction; direct current combined with a smaller value of alternating current.

pulse. A momentary sharp change in voltage or current.

pump load. The brake horsepower (kw output) required to drive a pump at rated speed and at the capacity requiring maximum power.

pump log conduit. In underground cable laying, a cheap and simple form of conduit composed of creosoted wood tubes.

puncture. A disruptive electrical discharge through insulation.

puncture voltage. A pressure which represents the strength of a dielectric, that is the highest voltage it will stand before failure.

pure resistance. Resistance in a nonreactive circuit.

push button. A cylindrically shaped part which is pressed by the finger to move the contact of a switch.

pyroelectricity. In certain crystaline bodies, electricity produced by unequally heating or cooling them.

pyrometer. A thermometer of any kind usable at relatively high temperatures.

Q

Q factor. A rating used to indicate characteristics of coils and resonant circuits; reactance divided by ohmic resistance.

quad. A structural unit employed in cable, consisting of four separately insulated conductors twisted together.

quadded cable. A cable in which some of the conductors are arranged in the form of quads.

quadrature. A quarter of a cycle phase difference. If the angle of lag or of lead between two sets of AC waves are 90 degrees, or a quarter circle, the waves are said to be in quadrature with each other.

qualified person. One familiar with the construction and operation of the equipment and the hazards involved.

quartz. A mineral which is not only a good insulator but desirable as a piezoelectric crystal.

quartz lamp. A mercury vapor lamp which uses in place of a glass container a tube of quartz. Higher temperatures can be maintained than with glass, hence stronger currents may be used.

quick-break. A switch or circuit breaker that has a high contact-opening speed.

quick-connect wiring termination. An electrical connection consisting of a male tab and female connector that can be readily engaged or disengaged without the use of a tool; referred to as a terminal.

quick-make. A switch or circuit breaker that has a high contact-closing speed.

R

R. Symbol for resistance.

R.P.M. An abbreviation for revolutions per minute.

raceway. An enclosed channel designed expressly for holding wires, cables, or bus bars, with additional functions as permitted by the Code.

raceway, office furnishings. A completely enclosed channel intended specifically for holding and routing of panel-system wiring, excluding communication and low voltage wiring.

rack, cable. A device secured to the wall to provide support for a cable raceway.

rack mounting. A method of mounting electric equipment in which metal panels supporting the equipment are attached to vertical steel channel rails or racks.

rad. A unit of time flux of light equal to a lumen per second; a lumen second.

radiant energy. Energy traveling in the form of electromagnetic waves.

radiant heat. Heat waves passing through space with the velocity of light, and giving the sensation of heat only when absorbed by the body through which they are passing.

radiant heater. A heater that dissipates an appreciable part of its heat by radiation rather than by conduction or convection.

radiation. The transmission of energy by ether vibrations.

radio frequency. Frequencies above about 100 KHz.

rainproof. So constructed, protected, or treated as to prevent rain from interfering with the successful operation of the apparatus under specified test conditions.

raintight. So constructed or protected that exposure to a beating rain will not result in the entrance of water under specified test conditions.

range. The pressure or temperature operating limits of a control.

range-adjusting screw. An adjusting screw used to change the operating set points of a control. Changes are limited to those within the control range.

rapid-start fluorescent lamp. A fluorescent lamp designed for operation with a ballast that provides a low voltage winding for preheating the electrodes and initiating the arc without a starting switch or the application of high voltage.

ratchet relay. A stepping relay actuated by an armature driven ratchet.

rated current. The current that a circuit breaker is intended to carry continuously without opening of the circuit.

rated load. The horsepower output for motors, kilowatt output for dynamos, and kilovolt ampere output for alternators.

rated locked rotor current. For squirrel cage induction or other internally short-circuited motors, the current taken from the line with the rotor locked and with rated voltage and frequency applied to the motor.

rating. A rating of a machine, apparatus, or device is a designated limit of operating characteristics based on definite conditions. Such operating characteristics as load, voltage, frequency, and the like, may be given in the rating.

rating, interrupting. The rating specifying the highest rms symmetrical, alternating current that the fuse is required to interrupt under the conditions of these requirements.

rating tests. Carrying-capacity, temperature, and clearing time current tests.

ratio. The relation of one number to another of the same kind. Thus the ratio of 240 to 120 is expressed as $240/120 = 2$; a ratio of 2 to 1.

ratio of transformer. The turn ratio, that is, the ratio of the number of turns in the full high voltage winding to that in the full low voltage winding. In a step down transformer, the number of primary turns divided by the number of secondary turns. In a step up transformer, the number of secondary turns divided by the number of primary turns.

Rawlplugs. A Rawlplug is an anchoring device made from stiffened strands of jute fiber. The screw entering the Rawlplug automatically threads it, which permits removal and replacement of the screw as often as needed. Used with materials such as: Brick, stone, concrete, drywall, glass, plaster, terra cotta, etc.

reactance. Opposition offered to the flow of AC by the inductance or capacity of a part; measured in ohms; designated by the letter X.

reactive load. A load which is either inductive or capacitive, that is, one in which the current is not in phase with the voltage.

reactive volt-amperes. A power value equal to the square root of the difference between the square of the apparent power and the square of the power. The reactive volt-amperes, when both current and voltage are sinusoidal, is equal to the volt-amperes times the sine of the angle which expresses the phase difference between current and voltage.

reactor. An induction or capacity unit, as an induction coil or a condenser.

215

readily accessible. Capable of being reached quickly for operation, renewal, or inspections, without requiring those to whom ready access is requisite to climb over or remove obstacles or to resort to portable ladders, chairs, etc.

receptacle. A receptacle is a contact device installed at the outlet for the connection of a single attachment plug.

receptacle circuit. A branch circuit to which only receptacle outlets are connected.

receptacle outlet. An outlet where one or more receptacles are installed.

reciprocal. In mathematics, the quotient arising by dividing unity by the number whose reciprocal is required.

reciprocating motor. An early type of motor whose armature acted with a reciprocating instead of rotary motion.

recording instrument. An instrument that makes a graphic record of the value of one or more quantities as a function of another variable, usually time.

recording voltmeter. A form of voltmeter designed to register the voltage measured by it.

recovery voltage. The voltage impressed upon the fuse after a circuit is cleared.

recreational vehicle. A vehicular type unit, primarily designed as temporary living quarters for recreational, camping, or travel use, that either has its own motive power or is mounted on or drawn by another vehicle.

rectangle. A rectangle is a parallelogram having its angles right angles.

rectification. The term used to designate the process by which electric energy is transferred from AC to DC.

rectified currents. Alternating currents which have been acted upon by a rectifying commutator and changed into direct pulsating currents.

rectifier. A device for converting AC to DC. The various kinds of rectifiers may be classes as: Mechanical, electromagnetic, electrolytic, mercury vapor, or mercury arc.

red pole. The north seeking pole of a magnet or magnetic needle, also known as the N, positive, marked, or boreal pole.

reduced voltage starter. A starter, the operation of which is based on the application of a reduced voltage to the motor.

reduced voltage tap. A tap on a transformer with which the unit may not be operated at full capacity without exceeding the specified temperature rise.

reducing coupling. A joint designed to make electrical connection between the ends of two conductors differing in size.

reduction. Changing terms of a problem into other terms of equivalent value to make it easier to solve.

redundant. Pertaining to characters that do not contribute to the information content. Redundant characters are often used for checking purposes or to improve reliability.

reed switch. A type of magnetically operated switch made by sealing two small steel leaves or reeds inside a glass tube. When a magnet is brought near, the reeds flex slightly, touching each other to complete the circuit. When the magnet is removed, the reeds spring apart, breaking the circuit.

reflection. The change of direction experienced by a ray of light or of other radiant energy, when it strikes a surface and is thrown back or reflected.

reflex angle. An angle greater than a straight angle.

refraction. The change in direction of a ray of light, heat, or electromagnetism when it enters obliquely, a medium of a different density from that through which it has previously moved.

refrigerant. The medium of heat transfer in a refrigerating system which picks up heat by evaporating at a low temperature and gives up heat by condensing at a higher temperature.

regeneration. Restoring a primary cell to activity after it has become polarized.

regulating relay. A type used to control the condition of a main circuit through control devices operated by a secondary circuit. They are used as feeder circuits or generator regulators, and differ from protective relays in that they have differentially arranged contacts, that is, arranged for contact on either side of a central or normal position.

regulation. The change in voltage which takes place between a condition of no load and of full load, or rated load, in a transformer, generator, or other source.

regulator. Any automatic or hand device for regulating a dynamo or motor; especially an electromagnetic device actuated by solenoids placed in the main circuit for automatic regulation.

reguline. In electrometallurgy, a term applied to metallic deposits which have all the characteristics of the pure metal.

relay. An electromagnetic device which permits control of current in one circuit by a much smaller current in another circuit.

relay contact. An electromagnetic mechanism which completes a local circuit when a current is passed through it.

reluctance. Magnetic resistance, that is, the resistance offered to the magnetic flux by the substance magnetized, being the ratio of the magnetic pressure to the magnetic flux. It is measured in oersteds. The reluctance is directly proportional to the length of the circuit, and inversely proportional to its cross sectional area.

reluctivity. The resistance per unit of length and unit cross section that a substance offers to being magnetized; specific magnetic resistance.

remanent flux. Residual magnetism, the magnetism which is retained by iron or steel after it has been magnetized and the magnetizing force has ceased to act upon it.

remote control. A method of operating machines from a distance with controls.

remote control circuit. Any electric circuit that controls any other circuit through a relay or equivalent device.

remote control device. A device for controlling equipment from a distance.

renewable cartridge fuse. A type of cartridge fuse having a screw cap at each end and arranged so that the fusible element is easily renewed.

repeatability. The ability of a control or interlock to maintain a constant set-point characteristic.

repeating relay. A relay employed in a telegraphic repeater to take a message from one wire and transmit it automatically to another wire.

repetend. A figure or set of figures continually repeated.

repulsion, electric. The action of a force by which two similarly charged bodies tend to repel each other.

repulsion-induction motor. An AC motor with two windings on the rotor, one a squirrel cage type, the other repulsion-start induction type.

repulsion motor. An AC motor in which the rotor is turned by repulsion between magnetic fields induced by supply current in the stator windings and other fields induced in the rotor winding. Supply current only to stator windings.

repulsion start induction motor. An AC motor that starts as a repulsion motor and after attaining speed runs as an induction motor; change over by automatic switch.

reset. To restore a device to a prescribed state.

residence. Any dwelling in which people reside.

residual current. The vector sum of the currents in several wires.

residual magnetism. The magnetism that remains in a piece of iron or steel when the magnetizing force is removed; as after the current stops flowing through the winding of an electromagnet. Residual magnetism in iron is of great importance in the working of the self-exciting dynamo, and is, indeed, the essential principle of this class of machine.

resilience. The act or quality of elasticity as understood by physicists; the property of springing back or recoiling upon removal of a pressure, as with a spring. Without special qualifications the term is understood to mean the work given out by a spring, or piece, strained similarly to a spring, after being strained to the extreme limit within which it may be strained again and again, without rupture or receiving permanent set.

resin. A class of vegetable products obtained from the sap of certain trees, especially the residue from distillation of pitch. Resin in its various forms is a dielectric, and is useful for insulating purposes; also spelled rosin.

resistance. The opposition offered by a substance or body to the passage through it of an electric current which converts electric energy into heat. Resistance is the reciprocal of conductance.

resistance braking. A system of dynamic braking in which electric energy generated by the traction motors is dissipated by means of a resistor.

resistance drop. The voltage drop in phase with the current.

resistance loss. A loss usually called the I^2R loss.

resistance starting. A form of reduced-voltage starting employing resistances that are short-circuited in one or more steps to complete the starting cycle.

resistance to ground. The ratio, at a point in a grounding system, of the component of the voltage to ground that is in phase with the ground current, to the ground current that produces it.

resistivity. The resistance of a centimeter cube of a substance to the flow of current between opposite sides; specific resistance.

resistor. An aggregation of one or more units possessing the property of electrical resistance. Resistors are used in electric circuits for the purpose of operation, protection, or control.

resistor material. For small motors, resistors are ordinarily made of a special wire wound on porcelain or asbestos tubing or some form of suitable base and then covered with cement. For intermediate sizes, ribbon resistor material or very fine cast iron grids are used, and for the heavy sizes, heavier cast iron grids are used almost exclusively. For very large motors these grids are parallel, to obtain the necessary current carrying capacity.

resonance. A phenomenon observed in AC circuits when capacity and inductance are present together in such proportion that they neutralize each other, making the spurious resistance of the circuit zero. An abnormal rise of current or voltage occurs in a part of the circuit, much in excess of the values supplied by the generating source. An electrical circuit is said to be in resonance with an impressed pressure, when the natural period of the circuit is equal to the period of the impressed pressure.

resonant circuit. An AC circuit in which the current is in phase with the voltage.

retardation. The tendency of electromagnetic inertia, or self-induction, to prevent an electric current beginning or ceasing instantaneously in a circuit.

retentivity. The power to hold residual magnetism, as shown by a magnetizable substance in its resistance to magnetization or demagnetization. Not all magnetic substances can become magnets permanently. Steel, lodestone, and nickel permanently retain the greater part of a magnetism imparted to them. Steel is magnetized with more difficulty than iron but retains the magnetism better than the latter. The power of resisting magnetism is called coercive force.

return circuit. That portion of an electric circuit through which the current is assumed to return to its starting point.

return ground. The ground return. The earth or ground used as a return in an electric circuit employing only one wire, the terminal being connected to water or gas pipes or to iron rods driven into the ground.

reverse contact. A contact that is closed when the operating unit is in the reverse position.

reverser. A switching device for interchanging electric circuits to reverse the direction of motor rotation.

reversible motor. An electric motor so adjusted that its direction of rotation may be reversed.

reversing switch. Any switch for reversing the direction of an electric current.

rheostat. A variable resistance mounted on a base or placed in a box and so arranged that the amount of resistance may be varied by moving a lever.

rhumbs of compass. The points of the compass.

ribbon coil. A coil having windings of insulated metal ribbons laid flat, in place of wires.

ribbon filament. A type of incandescent lamp filament as distinguished from the commonly used wire filament (of incandescent lamps); a filament consisting of a flat ribbon of tungsten, either flat to present a smooth surface to certain optical devices, or crimped, saw tooth fashion, to obtain the benefit of multiple reflections between the surface faces of the crimped sections in raising the brightness of the filament for any given power consumption.

ridged conductor. A ridge or stripe molded into the plastic insulation of one conductor on some twisted pair or parallel conductor wire. Permits polarity identification without stripping the wire.

right-hand rule. A rule to determine the direction of magnetic field around a conductor carrying a current. The thumb of the right hand is placed along the conductor, pointing in the direction in which the current is flowing. Then if the fingers are partly closed, the fingertips will point in the direction of the magnetic whirls.

right line. Straight line.

rigid metal conduit. A raceway specially constructed for the purpose of the pulling in or the withdrawing of wires or cables after the conduit is in place and made of metal pipe of standard weight and thickness permitting the cutting of standard threads.

ripple. The AC component from a DC power supply arising from sources within the power supply.

riser cable. The vertical portion of a house cable extending from one floor to another. In addition, the term is sometimes applied to other vertical sections of cable and raceway.

risers. In wiring, conductors rising vertically from one floor to another.

risk of shock, wiring systems. A risk of electric shock is considered to exist in any accessible connective part of a system if a potential greater than 42.4 volts peak (30 volts rms) exists, and the available current through a 1500 ohm resistor connected between (1) the part and the other accessible connective parts, or (2) between the part and ground, is more than 5 milliamperes.

R.M.A. color guide. A standard method of designating resistor values by colored markings. (Radio Manufacturers Association).

rodding a conduit. The process of drawing a cable through a conduit by first pushing through a series of interlocking rods and then pulling out the rods, the cable being attached to the end of the rods.

Romex. Trade name for Code type NM nonmetallic-sheathed cable.

roof truss. A set of tension and compression pieces so arranged as to support the weight of the roof.

root mean square (rms). The square root of the mean value of the square of a variable quantity. This function is particularly used in AC measurements, especially those of current and voltage. The mean value of these quantities being zero, the most readily measured function of them is the mean square value. Instruments for measuring the mean square usually have their scales marked to indicate the root mean square. When the value of an AC voltage or current is mentioned without qualification, it is usually to be understood to mean the root mean square value. The effective value, which is .707 of the peak value.

rope lay cable. A single conductor cable composed of a central core surrounded by one or more layers of helically-laid groups of wires. This kind of cable differs from concentric lay cable in that the main strands are themselves stranded.

rosette. A small two piece insulator in which connection is made between wiring and drop cords attached to the wiring. Rosettes are made of porcelain in two parts called the base and the cap. Although rosettes may be obtained either fused or unfused, the fused type is seldom used.

rosin. A flux (paste) used in soldering.

rotary converter. The synchronous or rotary converter consists of a synchronous motor and a dynamo combined in one machine. It resembles a dynamo with an unusually large commutator and an auxiliary set of collector rings. On the collector ring side it operates as a synchronous motor, while on the commutator side as a dynamo. Also called the synchronous converter.

rotary inverter. A machine that combines both motor and generator action in one armature winding connected to both a commutator and slip rings, and is excited by one magnetic field. It is normally used to change AC to DC.

rotary switch. A multicircuit switch having one contact on a pivoted arm and the other contacts placed radially around the pivot so that the contact arm may be rotated to touch any of the other contacts.

rotometer. A device used for linear measurement.

rotor. The member that rotates in a machine, generator, or motor.

rotor and stator. In some types of AC motor the function of the two parts is not well defined and where there is any chance of misunderstanding, the terms stator and rotor should be used. For instance, the rotor of a self-starting synchronous motor acts as an armature in starting (currents being induced in the squirrel cage bars), and as a field in running when the exciting current is turned on. Where there is no doubt as to function, the terms armature and field should be used.

roughing in. Installation of all concealed electrical wiring; includes all electrical work done before finishing.

round conductor. Either a solid or stranded conductor of which the cross section is substantially circular.

rubber. As applied to insulation, rubber is used in many ways. In the form of a thin plastic mass it may be laid over a wire and then vulcanized. It may be used as tape for direct insulation or for making joints. As vulcanite or ebonite it may be used as plates, tubes, rods, switch handles, etc.

rubber covered wire. A conductor for interior wiring consisting of a tinned copper wire with a rubber covering, protected by an outside braiding of cotton saturated with a preservative compound.

rubber tape. A specially prepared insulating, adhesive tape impregnated or coated with india rubber.

run winding. The winding in an electric motor that provides the power for turning the rotor during operation. It has the larger wire of the two windings.

S

S. Symbol for south pole of a magnet.

safe carrying capacity of wires. The maximum current strength that a conductor can safely carry without dangerous heating.

safety enclosed switchboard. A dead front switchboard with an enclosure on the back and sides. The front may be either detachable or fixed.

safety factor. Properly called factor of safety.

safety gap. A device employed on gap arresters, permitting a discharge to ground in case of an abnormal surge of voltage during a thunderstorm.

safety lamp. An incandescent lamp specially designed for use in mines and similar places where there is danger of firedamp or other explosive conditions.

safety outlet. Also termed "ground outlet"; an outlet with a polarized receptacle for equipment grounding.

sag. The difference in elevation between the highest point of support of the conductor and the lowest point of the conductor in the span.

salient poles. The poles of a dynamo or motor-field magnet occurring at the ends of the pole pieces, as distinguished from consequent poles.

salt. In chemistry, the neutral compound formed by the union of an acid and a base; thus, sulphuric acid and iron form the salt of sulphate of iron or green vitriol.

sand barrel setting. In pole line construction in loose or sandy soil, a barrel filled with earth used as a base into which the butt of the pole is set.

sand bending. The process of bending conduits or other pipes after having first filled them with sand and plugged the ends.

sash lines. In pole line construction, ropes employed to raise telephone and power poles of such size and weight as to require the use of a derrick.

saturable reactor. A control device that uses a small DC current to control a large AC current by controlling core flux density.

saturated flux. Lines of magnetic force sufficient to produce in a magnet a state of saturation.

saturated solution. A liquid which holds, in solution, all that it can dissolve of a substance at a given temperature.

saturation. The degree of magnetic force which can be permanently imparted to the core of a magnet; magnetic saturation.

saturation of coil. In ignition, the electrical state of a coil when the current in a primary coil, or in the primary winding of a secondary coil reaches full strength due to the impressed voltage so that at "break" the coil will produce the maximum arc or spark respectively. When the coil has reached this state it is said to be built up.

saw, electric. A platinum wire heated to incandescence by the electric current for the purpose of cutting certain substances.

scalar. In physics, a quantity which has magnitude, or magnitude and sign only, without direction, such as density, mass, energy, etc., as distinguished from a vector quantity.

scheduled outage. An outage that results when a component is deliberately taken out of service at a selected time, usually for purposes of construction, preventive maintenance, or repair.

schematic diagram. A diagram that shows, by means of graphic symbols, the electric connections and functions of a specific circuit. The schematic diagram traces the circuit and its functions without regard to actual physical size, shape, or location of the component devices or parts. Should not be confused with a wiring diagram.

scott-connected transformer. An assembly for transforming from three phase to two phase or from two phase to three phase.

SCR. Semiconductor controlled rectifier.

screen. A port cover with multiple openings used to limit the entry of foreign objects.

screw cleat. In indoor wiring, a cleat carrying the necessary screws for quickly retaining it to the walls.

screw pitch gauge. A small instrument furnished with a number of thread gauges, usually ranging from 28 to 6 per inch, for ascertaining the pitch or number of threads per inch of any given screw.

screw threads. A helical groove of sufficient turns cut at the end of a bolt or through the hole in a nut for the purpose of fastening the two pieces together, called a male and female thread, respectively; also called the outside and inside threads.

sealable equipment. Equipment enclosed in a case or cabinet that is provided with a means of sealing or locking so that live parts cannot be made accessible without opening the enclosure. The equipment may or may not be operable without opening the enclosure.

sealed. Provided with special seals to minimize either the leakage of the internal coolant out of the enclosure or the leakage of medium surrounding the enclosure into the machine.

sealed refrigeration compressor. A mechanical compressor consisting of a compressor and a motor, both of which are enclosed in the same sealed housing, with no external shaft or shaft seals, the motor operating in the refrigerant atmosphere.

sealing gap. The distance between the armature and the center of the core of a magnetic contactor when the contacts first touch each other.

sealing voltage or current. The voltage or current necessary to seat the armature of a magnetic contactor from the position at which the contacts first touch each other, under conditions of normal operating temperature.

sealing wax. A mixture, as of shellac and turpentine with a pigment, as vermillion or lampblack, that is fluid when heated, but quickly solidifies on cooling; used for making seals.

search light. A powerful electric lantern containing a focusing arc lamp between a system of reflectors and a lens, for projecting the light to a great distance.

secant. A straight line cutting a curve at two or more points. A straight line drawn from the center of a circle through one end of a circular arc to a tangent drawn from the other end of the arc. The trigonometric function that for an acute angle is the ratio of the hypotenuse of a right triangle of which the angle is considered part and the leg adjacent to the angle.

secohm. A term proposed for the practical unit of self-induction, now called the henry.

second. (a) The unit of time. (b) A unit of circular measure; one degree equals 3,600 seconds.

secondary. A term commonly used for a secondary coil.

secondary ampere turns. The number of ampere turns in the secondary coil of a transformer or induction coil.

secondary battery. A battery that can be recharged after its chemical energy is depleted.

secondary cell. The proper name for the so-called storage cell.

secondary coil. A type of induction coil consisting of a long iron wire core upon which is wound primary and secondary windings. It works on the principle of mutual induction. Its main objective is to considerably step up the voltage. Distinguish between secondary coil and transformer.

secondary current. The current induced in the secondary of a transformer or induction coil.

secondary distribution system. A low-voltage AC system that connects the secondaries of distribution transformers to the consumers' services.

secondary main. In electric lighting, the main coming from the secondary coil of a transformer or converter, which conveys current to the lamps.

secondary winding. In a secondary induction coil, the winding in which induction takes place. In an ignition coil it is the high tension winding; in a house lighting transformer, the low tension winding.

sector cable. A multiple conductor cable in which the cross section of each multiwire conductor is substantially a sector, an ellipse, or a figure intermediate between them.

sediment. In a storage battery, loosened or worn out particles of active material fallen to the bottom of cells; frequently called "mud." A first class storage cell will have plenty of sediment space.

Seebeck effect. A thermoelectric effect discovered by Seebeck. He observed that an electric current was produced in a closed circuit by heating a point of two dissimilar metals. The two metals producing this effect are known as a thermoelectric couple.

seesawing. A term applied to the state of two parallel connected alternators running out of step, or not synchronously; hunting.

segment. The portion of a circle included between a chord and the arc which it subtends.

selector switch. A switch arranged to permit connecting a conductor to any one of a number of other conductors.

selenium eye. A model of the human eye constructed for photoelectrical experiment purposes, having a retina of selenium connected in circuit with a battery and galvanometer.

self-cooling transformer. A transformer which can be sufficiently cooled by contact of its coils with the air, or by merely filling the case with oil, without resorting to a forced circulation.

self-excitation. Magnetizing the field magnets of a dynamo by means of currents generated in its own armature. It is made possible by virtue of residual magnetism in the frame and pole pieces of the machine.

self-induction. The property of an electric current by virtue of which it tends to resist any change of value. It is sometimes spoken of as electromagnetic inertia and is analogous to the mechanical inertia of matter. Self-induction is due to the action of current upon itself during variations in strength.

self-lubricating bearing. A bearing lined with a material containing its own lubricant, such that little or no additional lubricating fluid need be added subsequently, to ensure satisfactory lubrication of the bearing.

self-supporting aerial cable. A cable consisting of one or more insulated conductors, factory assembled with a messenger that supports the assemblage, and that may or may not form a part of the electric circuit.

selsyn. A system comprising a generator and a motor so connected by a wire that the angular rotation or position in the generator is reproduced simultaneously in the motor (self-synchronizing). Also called synchro.

semantics. The relationship between symbols and their meanings.

semaphore. An apparatus for exhibiting signals and used in the railroad block system.

semiautomatic. Combining manual and automatic features so that a manual operation is required to supply to the automatic feature the actuating influence that causes the automatic feature to function.

semiconducting material. A conducting medium in which the conduction is by electrons, and holes, and whose temperature coefficient of resistivity, is negative over some temperature range below the melting point.

semiconductor. A name given to substances having only moderate power of transmitting electricity, and which may be said in that respect to, stand midway between conductors and insulators.

semidirect lighting. Lighting that the luminaires distribute 60 to 90 percent of the light downward and the balance upward.

sensible heat. That part of heat which produces a rise in temperature, as shown by a thermometer, as distinguished from latent heat.

sensitive relay. A relay that operates on a low power input.

separable core. A core, as of an electromagnet which may be readily withdrawn from the coils.

separate touch. A method of magnetizing a steel bar, in which two bar magnets with their opposite poles near together, are brought into contact with the middle of the bar and drawn apart toward the ends and back several times, leaving off at the middle. This method is also called divided touch.

separately derived systems. A premises wiring system whose power is derived from generator, transformer, or converter windings and has no direct electrical connection, including a solidly connected grounded circuit conductor, to supply conductors originating in another system.

separator. In a storage battery, an insulator between plates of opposite polarity; usually of wood, rubber, or a combination of both. Separators are generally corrugated or ribbed to insure proper distance between plates and to avoid too great of a displacement of electrolyte.

sequencer. A device designed to start or stop pieces of equipment in a predetermined sequence. It is usually used on multistage systems for capacity control.

sequential. If the signal elements are transmitted at the same time over a multiwire circuit, the transmission is said to be coincident.

series AC motor. A type identical with the series DC motor, but having all the iron of the magnetic circuit laminated. Sometimes a neutralizing winding is used.

series and parallel coupling of dynamos. Since the output of a dynamo is made up of two factors; (a) the pressure and (b) current, it follows that the output of a machine may be enlarged by increasing either one or the other, or both at the same time. As, however, the systems of distribution in use at the present time involve the maintenance of either a constant current or a constant pressure in a circuit, the methods of coupling dynamos together resolve themselves into two kinds, corresponding to the systems of distribution, parallel and series connections. In coupling two or more machines in parallel, the pressures of all the machines are kept at a constant value, while the output of the plant is increased in proportion to the current capacities of the machines in the circuit. In the series coupling, the current capacity of the plant is kept at a constant value, while the output is increased in proportion to the pressures of the machines in circuit.

series booster. An automatic booster which adjusts its voltage to produce the proper ratio of charge or discharge with varying external load, and it also tends to maintain a constant voltage across the line, under all conditions of change in circuit.

series circuit. A circuit supplying energy to a number of loads connected in series, that is, the same current passes through each load in completing its path to the source of supply.

series DC motor. A motor in which the field magnet, coils, consisting of a few turns of thick wire, are connected in series with the armature so that the whole current supplied to the motor passes through the field coils as well as the armature.

series DC motor characteristics. The field strength increases with the current, since the latter flows through the magnet coils. If the motor is run on a constant voltage circuit, with light load, it will run at a very high speed; again, if the motor is loaded heavily, the speed will be much less than before. Series motors should not be employed where the load may be entirely removed because they would attain a dangerous speed. They should not be used for driving by means of belts, because a sudden release of the load due to a mishap to the belt would cause the motor to "run away" in speed.

series gap of lightning arrester. A spark gap connected in series with a lightning arrester which keeps the circuit through the lightning arrester open under normal conditions, but closes the circuit for the lightning discharge by sparking over.

series lighting. A method of lighting in which the lamps are connected in series; the constant current series system.

series multiple. Series parallel.

series parallel circuit. An electric circuit containing groups of parallel connected receptive devices, the groups being arranged in the circuit in series; a series multiple circuit.

series winding. The winding of a series machine, consisting of a few turns of thick insulated wire, wound upon the field magnets and connected in series with the armature, so that the whole of the current passes through the coils into the external circuit.

series-wound motor. A commutator motor in which the field circuit and armature circuit are connected in series.

serrated. Toothed or notched along the edge, like a saw. The word is derived from the Latin: serra, a saw.

service. The conductors and equipment for delivering energy from the electricity supply system to the wiring system of the premises served.

service block. In electric distribution, a branch block containing safety fuses for connecting service wires to a main.

service cable. Service conductors made up in the form of a cable.

service conductors. The supply conductors that extend from the street main or from transformers to the service equipment of the premises supplied.

service connection. That portion of the supply conductors which extends from the street main or duct or transformers to the service switch, switches, or switchboard of the building supply.

service drop. The overhead service conductors from the last pole or other aerial support to and including the splices, if any, connecting to the service-entrance conductors at the building or other structure.

service-entrance conductors, overhead system. The service conductors between the terminals of the service equipment and a point usually outside the building, clear of building walls, where joined by a tap or splice to the service drop.

service-entrance conductors, underground system. The service conductors between the terminals of the service equipment and the point of connection to the service lateral.

service equipment. The necessary equipment, usually consisting of a circuit breaker or switch and fuses, and their accessories, located near the point of entrance of supply conductors to a building or other structure, or an otherwise defined area, and intended to constitute the main control and means of cutoff of the supply.

service factor. Service factor means that the motor can be allowed to develop more than its rated or nameplate HP, without causing undue deterioration of the insulation. The service factor is a margin of safety.

service lateral. The underground service conductors between the street main, including any risers at a pole or other structure or from transformers, and the first point of connection to the service-entrance conductors in a terminal box or meter or other enclosure with adequate space, inside or outside the building wall. Where there is no terminal box, meter, or other enclosure with adequate space, the point of connection shall be considered to be the point of entrance of the service conductors into the building.

service main. In electric distribution, the wire which leads from the street main into the consumer's premises.

237

serviceman. A person who may periodically open an appliance to repair or maintain electrical or mechanical components.

service raceway. The raceway that encloses the service-entrance conductors.

serving. A wrapping applied over the core of a cable before the cable is leaded, or over the lead if the cable is armored.

serving mallet. A mallet for laying on closely and evenly, the coating of jute, paper, or other insulating material employed to wrap a cable core before the sheath is applied; a serving tool.

servo. A device used to convert a small movement into one of greater movement or force.

servomechanism. A closed-loop system that produces a force to position an object in accordance with the information that originates at the input.

set point. A predetermined value to which a control or interlock is adjusted and at which it performs its intended function.

set screw. A screw with a pointed or cupped end, used to secure a pulley upon a shaft or for like purposes.

sextipolar. Having six poles.

sextant. An optical instrument for measuring the angular displacement between two distant objects.

shackle. A form of swinging insulator bracket for use upon a pole where an angle occurs in the line.

shade. A screen made of diffusing material that is designed to prevent a light source from being directly visible at normal angles of view.

shaded-pole motor. A shaded-pole motor is a single-phase induction motor provided with an auxiliary short-circuited winding or windings displaced in magnetic position from the main winding.

shading coil. In a split phase motor, an auxiliary coil used to split the phase in starting.

shadowgraph. In testing an electric flatiron, records made at short intervals of the ability of the iron to scorch paper to show its power to hold heat.

shadows, electric. The current of electrified air from a charged pointed conductor will produce a charge upon the surface of any insulating body, such as a plate of ebonite or glass, held a few inches away. If a slip of mica or glass is interposed between the surfaces, against which the wind is directed and the point where it comes from, an electric shadow will be formed on the surfaces at the part so screened.

shaft. That part of a rotor that carries other rotating members and that is supported by bearings in which it can rotate.

shallow water cable. A cable designed to be laid in comparatively shallow water, and specially protected against wear upon a rocky bottom by the provision of extra sheathing.

sheath. The final protective coating applied to a cable.

sheating. First covering of boards or paneling nailed to the outside of the wood studs of a frame building.

shed of insulator. The petticoat of a line wire insulator.

sheet lightning. A form of lightning seen as a broad flash illuminating a large area of the clouds, and apparently unaccompanied by thunder, probably due to reflection from a distant storm.

sheet metal. The term sheet is applied to material (with the exception of lead) having a thickness less than #12 U.S. gauge.

shellac. A commercial form of a resinous substance found upon certain tropical trees, and prepared for the market in thin shells; when dissolved in alcohol it forms shellac varnish, which is useful in electrical work for its insulating properties.

shell core. A core for a transformer or reactor consisting of three legs, with the winding located on the center leg.

shell transformer. A type in which the core is in the form of a shell, being built around and through coils. A shell transformer has, as a rule, fewer turns and a higher voltage per turn than the core type.

shielded conductor cable. A cable in which the insulated conductors are enclosed in a conducting envelope.

shims. Pieces of sheet metal used to adjust a bearing.

shock, electric. A painful and sometimes dangerous shock to the human system, produced by a discharge through the body of static or current electricity, especially when of high voltage.

shoe. In the third rail system of electric traction, cast iron rubbing shoes carried on insulated spring supports, by means of which electric contact is made with the third rail.

shore feeder. Permanently installed conductors from a distribution switchboard to a connection box for the attachment of power supply leads to a ship from a source on shore.

short. A contraction sometimes used among repairmen for short circuit.

short-circuit. A fault in an electric circuit or apparatus due usually to imperfect insulation, such that the current follows a by-path and inflicts damage or is wasted.

short-circuit protection. Any automatic current-limiting system that enables a power supply to continue operating at a limited current, and without damage, into any output overload including short-circuits.

short-time duty. Operation at a substantially constant load for a short and definite specified time.

show window. Any window used or designed to be used for the display of goods or advertising material, whether it is fully or partly enclosed or entirely open at the rear and whether or not it has a platform raised higher than the street floor level.

shunt. (a) In an electric circuit, a branch conductor joining the main circuit at two points and forming a parallel or derived circuit, so that the current is divided, a part passing through the branch and a part through the main circuit. (b) To introduce a shunt into an electric circuit.

shunt circuit. A shunt; a by-path provided in an electric circuit so that only a portion of the current shall pass through it. A shunt is employed with dynamos, motors, and electrical instuments for deflecting a small part of the current where the entire current strength is not required.

shunt control. A method of controlling motors employing the shunt method of transition from series to parallel connections of the motors.

shunt for ammeter. A shunt of low resistance and small temperature coefficient introduced into the circuit of an ammeter in order that the current flowing in the moving coil of the instrument may be proportional to that in the main circuit. The shunt consists of two heavy terminal blocks of copper or brass between which are brazed thin sheets of resistance metal such as manganin or constantan, offering a large radiating surface to the air.

shunt law. The currents in two parallel circuits are inversely proportional to their resistances.

shunt trip. A release energized by a source of voltage. The voltage may be derived either from the main circuit or from an independent source.

shunt-trip recloser. A recloser in which the tripping mechanism, by releasing the holding means, permits the main contacts to open, with both the tripping mechanism and the contact-opening mechanism deriving operating energy from other than the main circuit.

shunt winding. The winding of a shunt machine consisting of a large number of turns of fine insulated copper wire, which is wound round the field magnets and connected to the brushes, as to form a shunt or "by-pass" to the brushes and external circuit. The object of using a shunt winding for field magnets of dynamos is that the machine may more readily excite its own fields at starting, and that the current may be produced before the rotating armature has fully taken up its speed.

shunt-wound motor. A DC motor in which the field circuit and armature circuit are connected in parallel.

side bracket. A form of bracket for supporting a single insulator upon the side of a pole or building.

sides of three-wire system. The positive and negative wires in the three-wire system of electric distribution.

sidewalk elevator. A freight elevator that operates between a sidewalk or other exterior to the building and floor levels inside the building below such area, that has no landing opening into the building at its upper limit of travel, and that is not used to carry automobiles.

siding. Finishing material that is nailed to the sheathing of a wood frame building and that forms the exposed surface.

Siemens armature. An early form of dynamo armature devised by Siemens in 1856. The armature is commonly known as the shuttle armature. A single coil of wire is wound in an "H" shaped groove, formed in a bobbin shaped core.

sign. A fixed, stationary, or portable, self-contained, electrically illuminated, utilization equipment with words or symbols designed to convey information or attract attention.

signal. A visual, audible, or other indication used to convey information.

signal circuit. Any electric circuit that supplies energy to an appliance that gives a recognizable signal. A doorbell is an example of a signal circuit.

signal elevator operation. A system of elevator control in which the elevator is started by the operator, but where the stopping is brought about as the result of pressing one of the signal buttons.

signaling circuit. Any electric circuit that energizes signaling equipment.

signal relay. An auxiliary relay which operates an audible or visible signal.

signal flasher. A device used for giving flashing and changeable effects to electric light signs.

signs. + (plus) and - (minus) for positive and negative respectively. These signs are descriptive of polarity.

silent discharge. A discharge of electricity which takes place from the tip of a pointed conductor when the charge has accumulated there, with so great a density, as to electrify the surrounding air. The particles of air fly off the repulsion and convey a part of the charge with them. It is usually known as a convective discharge and acts silently in contrast with the noise of a disruptive discharge.

silk enamel wire. A wire covered with one or more servings of white tram silk. Combining the high dielectric of the enamel with the protection from abrasion afforded by the silk servings, it offers the utmost degree of insulation with but little sacrifice of winding space.

silver. A precious metal of a white lustrous appearance. It is the best conductor of electricity and is taken as a standard with which all other conductors are compared. As compared to copper, the relative conductivity is in the ratio of 100 to 75, silver being 100.

silvering. The application of a thin conducting film of silver by chemical reduction upon a plastic or wax matrix.

silver plating. Electroplating articles composed of a base metal with a coating of silver by immersing them in a silver bath, opposite sheets of silver, which form the anodes of the electrolytic cell, the articles to be plated being the cathodes.

simple fraction. One expressed by a numerator and denominator (each being a whole number) as distinguished from a decimal fraction.

simple immersion. A method of obtaining a metallic coating upon an article by simply dipping the article in a bath of melted metal.

simplex circuit. A circuit derived from a pair of wires by using the wires in parallel with ground return.

simplex two-circuit winding. A form of armature winding having only two paths through the armature, and requiring only two sets of brushes, whatever the number of poles.

simultaneous equations. Two separate equations considered together as representing simultaneous relations between unknown quantities.

sine curve. A wave like curve used to represent the changes in strength and direction of an alternating current. The current begins at zero, rises to a maximum, decreases again to zero, and increases to a maximum in the opposite direction, tracing a waving line in which the horizontal distances represent the varying values of voltage. It is called a sine curve because its' perpendicular at any point is proportional to the sine of the angle corresponding to that point.

sine law. A law that the force acting upon a body is directly proportional to the angle of deflection if, (a) the controlling force has a constant magnitude and direction, and (b), the deflecting force is uniform in direction with respect to the body acted upon.

sine wave. The changes during one cycle of an alternating current corresponding to sine values of the sine curve.

single and double break switches. The distinction is that the one breaks the circuit at one point only, while the other breaks it at two points. If the circuit is opened at two points in series, at the same instant, the voltage is divided between the two breaks, and the length to which the current will maintain an arc at either break is reduced to one-half; thus there is less chance of burning the metal of the switch.

single break switch. One which breaks a circuit at a single contact. Suited for light duty.

single circuit. An electric circuit containing no branch circuits, as distinguished from a divided circuit.

single-element fuse. A fuse having a current-responsive element, comprising one or more parts with single fusing characteristic.

single phase. A term applied to a simple alternating current of uniform frequency as distinguished from polyphase currents.

single-phase circuit. An AC circuit consisting of two or three intentionally interrelated conductors.

single-phase systems. There are various arrangements for transmission and distribution classes as single-phase systems. Thus, single-phase current may be conveyed to the various receiving units by the well known circuit arrangement known as series, parallel, series parallel. Again, single-phase current may be transmitted by two wires and distributed by three wires. This method of treating the neutral wire is only permissible where there is very little unbalancing, that is, where the load is kept practically the same on both sides of the neutral.

245

single-phase three-wire circuit. A single-phase circuit consisting of three conductors, one of which is identified as the neutral conductor, white in color.

single phase transformer. One having only one set of primary and secondary terminals, and in which the fluxes in the one or more magnetic circuits are all in phase.

single pole switch. A type of switch designed to control one circuit.

single service. One service only supplying a consumer.

single throw switch. One in which the movement of the blade from the off position to a live contact is limited to one direction.

single wound wire. A conductor wrapped with only one layer of insulation.

sinuous current. An electric current flowing through a spiral conductor.

sinusoidal. Having the form of a sine wave. A curve of sines.

sinusoidal alternator. An alternator which generates simple harmonic or sinusoidal currents.

sinusoidal currents. In electrotherapeutics, currents of the alternating group, which comprise the rapid sinusoidal, the interrupted sinusoidal, rapid sinusoidal wave, and the rapid sinusoidal wave sustained peak, all of which are obtained from the basic current, the rapid sinusoidal and none of which possesses any polar effect, although the negative impulse is 1/120th of a second in duration and produces a certain amount of skin effect.

siren. A signaling device having a perforated rotating disc or discs through which compressed air is discharged in rapid succession to produce a continuous loud whistle.

six-phase system. A system of electrical distribution of polyphase currents, consisting of two, three-phase systems in opposition to each other.

sixteenth bend. In pipe fitting, a pipe bend which makes an arc of 22 1/2 degrees and which, therefore, connects pipes which diverge at that angle.

S joint. A method of connecting two surfaces, which are at right angles to each other, by means of a doubly bent strip, somewhat like the letter S reversed.

skin. The voltage in a high frequency AC circuit producing skin currents.

skin currents. High frequency, alternating currents which are confined mainly to the outer surface of the conductor instead of passing uniformly through the cross section of the wire.

skin effect. The tendency of alternating currents to avoid the central portion of solid conductors and to flow or pass mostly through the outer portion. The so-called skin effect becomes more pronounced as the frequency is increased. It is due to eddy currents induced in the conductor. It results in an apparent increase of resistance.

slack cable switch. A safety elevator switch used on a drum type elevator to open the control circuit in case of slack rope caused by the car or counter-weight being caught in the guides.

sled. In the conduit system of electric traction, a form of contact plow which, instead of being pushed along the conducting wire, is drawn over the wire after the car.

sleeve bearing. A bearing with a cylindrical inner surface in which the journal of a rotor shaft rotates.

sleeve, splicing. Also termed "connector"; a metal sleeve slipped over and secured to the butted ends of conductors to make a joint that provides good electrical connection.

sleeve wiping. In cable jointing, slip the lead sleeve into position and dress the end down to fit over the cable. Apply gummed paper about 3 inches wide on the cable and on the sleeve, in order to confine the wiping to the proper joint. Both ends of the sleeve should be soldered to the lead sheath of the cable with a wiped joint.

sleeve wire. A circuit conductor connected to the sleeve of a plug or jacket.

slide resistance. A form of rheostat employed in telegraphy in which the coils are arranged in a circle and controlled by a pair of contact arms, each capable of moving over a half circle of contact points.

slide rule. A mechanical device for performing operations of arithmetic in calculating, such as multiplication, division, involution, etc. A slide rule has four scales designated by the letters A, B, C, and D. The two outer scales are stationary, but the two inner scales are on a tongue arranged to slide between the two outer scales.

sliding contact. An electrical contact obtained by a sliding motion of one conductor over another.

sliding joint. In pipe fitting, an expansion joint.

sling psychometer. An instrument used in air conditioning. It consists of two accurately graduated mercury thermometers mounted on a metal strip and equipped with a swivel handle or chain to permit whirling. To observe the wet and dry bulb temperatures of the air, the wet bulb is thoroughly saturated with clean water, preferably distilled. The instrument is then whirled at a rate of 100 rpms or more.

slings. In electroplating, looped pieces of insulated copper wire employed for suspending articles in the plating baths; also called slinging wires.

slip. In an induction motor, the difference in speed between the armature and the rotating magnetic field or synchronous speed. This is a vital factor in the operation of an induction motor, since there must be slip in order that the armature inductors shall cut magnetic lines to induce currents therein, so as to create a driving torque. Slip varies from about 2 to 5 percent of synchronous speed, depending upon the size of the motor.

slip-ring motor. An external resistance induction motor. In this motor the starting torque and the starting current are under the control of the operator and may be varied at his will. The slip-ring motor accordingly permits the heaviest loads to be started slowly and smoothly with no objectionable line disturbances. It is adapted to variable speed service. Wide variations of speed may be obtained without complicated arrangements.

slip-rings. Insulated rings mounted upon an alternator shaft to receive direct current for the revolving field.

slope. In a magnetic field, the direction in which the intensity of the field of force diminishes.

slotted conduit. In the conduit system of electrical traction, a conduit for carrying the conducting wire, usually placed midway between the tracks and furnished with a continuous slot through which connection is made with the car motors.

slotted core armature. A type having grooves or slots cut through the core laminae and having the advantage that the "teeth," or metal left between the slots, to protect the inductors, retain them in place against the electrical drag and centrifugal force, and the construction permits a reduction of air gap to a minimum, thus reducing the amount of copper required for the field.

slow-blow fuse. A fuse that is designed not to blow or open as rapidly as a regular fuse. This type of fuse can better withstand momentary surges such as the starting of a motor.

slow burning construction. A type or class of construction suitable for mill buildings, in which heavy hardwood timbers are employed fitting closely into each other, without crevices for the accumulation of dust, for the passage of air or for affording play to flames of a fire.

slow burning wire. One that will not carry fire. The covering consists of layers of cotton or other thread, all the interstices of which are filled with the fireproofing compound, or of material having equivalent fire resisting and insulating properties. The outer layer is braided and specially designed to withstand abrasion. The thickness of insulation must not be less than that required for slow burning weatherproof wire and the outer surface must be finished smooth and hard.

smashing point. In incandescent lighting, the point reached when it becomes more economical to install a new lamp than to continue burning a lamp which has passed its useful life. This point can be calculated when the rate at which the candlepower falls off, the watts per candle increase, and the cost of lamp and electric energy are known.

smelting, electric. The working of mineral ores by the use of the electric arc, in which the ore mixed with carbon is placed in a suitable furnace between carbon electrodes of large size and fused by the arc produced by a current of intense strength.

snake. A steel wire or flat ribbon with a hook at one end, used to draw wires through conduit, etc.

snapper. In cable laying, an arrangement consisting of automatic metal jaws used at the end of a sounding line for the purpose of bringing up samples of the sea bottom.

snap switch. A switch designed for installation in a box or for surface mounting, rated in amperes and volts.

sneak current. An abnormal current on a telephone conductor that is not sufficient to open a fuse wire or line fuse and is not driven by a voltage that is high enough to cause the arrester to operate.

snips. Small, stout, short lipped shears, used especially for cutting sheet metal and wire.

soakage. (a) A term sometimes applied to the small charge of electricity which remains in a Leyden jar or other condenser after it has been discharged. (b) It is also a term used for the residual magnetism which is retained by a magnet after the magnetizing force has ceased to act upon it.

soaking, charge. A low 24 hour rate storage battery charge intended to remove excess sulphate from the plates.

soapstone. Steatite, a massive variety of talc. It is often used for switch bases and switchboard panels not requiring finish, as it is superior to slate in insulating properties.

socket. A device for mechanical support of a lamp and for connection to the electrical supply.

socket adapter. A connecting fitting which enables a tube having one type base to be connected to a socket made for a different type base.

socket extension. A device which makes it possible to use a lamp in a reflector which was designed for a lamp of longer light center.

socket lamp. An incandescent electric lamp mounted upon a socket.

soda or sodium. One of the two principal alkaline metals, found nowhere uncombined, but most abundantly diffused as a compound.

soffit. The underside of a stair, arch, or cornice.

soft and hard copper. In electric wiring, ordinary pure copper is comparatively soft, and a span of any considerable weight cannot sustain its own weight. In a gale, the wind pressure greatly increases the stress upon the wire.

251

soft iron. A general term applied to both wrought iron and cast iron which can be shaped with ordinary cutting tools or abraded readily with files.

solar photovoltaic system. The total components and subsystems, which in combination, convert solar energy into electrical energy suitable for connection to a utilization load.

solder. Any fusible alloy used to unite different metal parts. In electrical, the solder used is practically always an alloy of tin and lead.

soldered joint. In wiring for maximum conductivity, joints should be soldered.

soldering. Briefly, the theory of soldering is that: As the solder adheres to and unites with the surface of the copper when the bit is tinned, so will it adhere to and unite the surfaces of the metals to be soldered. The operations to be performed in soldering are: (1) cleaning the surface to be soldered; (2) heating the bit; (3) tinning the bit; (4) applying the flux; (5) picking up the solder; (6) applying the bit.

soldering flux. A substance applied to a metal to make solder flow readily on its surface. The action of the flux is largely that of cleaning the surface, and of reducing any oxide on the surface to the metallic state.

solderless connector. Any device that connects wires together without solder; wire nuts are the most common type used.

solenoid. A spiral of conducting wire, wound cylindrically so that when an electric current passes through it, its turns are nearly equivalent to a succession of parallel circular circuits, and it acquires magnetic properties similar to those of a bar magnet.

soleplate. Horizontal bottom member of a wood stud partition.

solid conductor. A conductor consisting of a single wire.

solid conduit. A conduit for underground wiring in which the conductors are permanently embedded in insulating material, preventing their removal.

solid earth. A term sometimes used for dead earth; a fault in an electric circuit due to the complete grounding of the line.

solid-state. An adjective used to describe a circuit, device, or system whose operation is dependent upon any combination of optical, electrical, or magnetic phenomena within a solid.

sonar. Apparatus or techniques whereby underwater acoustic energy is employed to obtain information regarding objects below the surface of the water.

source. The origin of something supplied as the source of the electric circuit; may be a dynamo, alternator, storage battery, etc.

southern lights. The aurora australis; the counterpart of the northern lights or aurora borealis, seen in the southern hemisphere in the direction of the south magnetic pole. It exhibits the same characteristics as the northern aurora, showing broad flashes or ribbons of waving light which are undoubtedly due to electrical causes.

space charge. The cloud of electrons existing in the space between the cathode and plate in a vacuum tube, formed by the electrons emitted from the cathode in excess of those immediately attracted to the plate.

spaced winding. A coil wound with adjacent turns spaced some distance from each other. The object of this spacing is to reduce distributed capacity.

spacing of wires. In wiring, the conductors should be so spaced as to lessen the tendency to leakage and to prevent the wires swinging together or against other objects.

spaghetti tubing. A lowbrow name for a varnished, impregnated, cloth tubing used to insulate radio wires.

spa, hot tub or. Terms used interchangeably to indicate a hydromassage tub intended for the immersion of persons in heated water, intended to be circulated in a closed system, and not intended to be drained and filled with each use. Such installations usually include a filter, heater (electric, solar, or gas), pump, and controls, and may also include lights and an air blower.

span. That part of any conductor, cable, or pole line between two consecutive points of support.

spare equipment. Equipment complete or in parts, on hand for repair or replacement of equipment.

spark. A discharge of electricity across a gap between two electrodes. The discharge is accompanied by heat and incandescence. Distinguish between spark and arc.

spark arrester. Wire netting used to screen the carbons of arc lamps to prevent the scattering of sparks from the arc.

spark coil. In ignition, a secondary coil for obtaining the high voltage necessary to produce the spark. It consists essentially of a core composed of a bundle of soft iron wires surrounded by two separate windings, a primary made up of a comparatively few turns of coarse insulated wire, and a secondary composed of very many turns of fine insulated wire, the two coils being insulated from each other.

special loop. A method of locating a faulty wire or cable where the length only is known and where there are two other wires which may be used to complete the loop. It is not necessary that the resistance of the faulty wire and the length and resistance of the other wires be known.

special permission. The written consent of the authority having jurisdiction.

specific gravity. The weight of a volume of a material compared to the weight of the same volume of water, at a given temperature.

specific heat. The amount of heat required to raise the temperature of a given weight of a substance one degree as compared with the amount of heat required to raise the temperature of the same weight of water one degree at some specified temperature.

specific resistance. The relative resistance of a substance to the passage of electricity, as referred to some standard substance.

spelter. Commercial zinc.

spelter solder. An alloy of copper and zinc, mixed together in various proportions, of needle-like or granular form. This is used in brazing and is the same as hard solder.

spent acid. An acid solution that has become exhausted so that it is no longer capable of performing chemical action.

sphere. A solid, every part of whose circumference is equidistant from a point within, called the center.

spider web coil. A flat coil formed by a spirally wound conductor. Also called a pancake coil.

spiral winding. A winding composed of spiral coils and used extensively for armature windings of alternators.

spirit level. One in which the adjustment to the horizon depends on the position of a bubble, or small vacant space, in the upper right side of a glass tube, which is slightly curved and nearly filled with alcohol or ether.

splashproof apparatus. Apparatus so constructed and protected that external splashing will not interfere with its successful operation.

splayed joint. A method of jointing a covered stranded cable, in which the covering is removed a short distance from each end, the separate wires opened out, the two sets brought end to end and laced together, and the whole secured with solder.

splice. A joint used for connecting conductors together.

split brush. Either an industrial or fractional-horsepower brush consisting of two pieces that are used in place of one brush.

split-conductor cable. A cable in which each conductor is composed of two or more insulated conductors normally connected in parallel.

split fitting. A conduit fitting split so that it can be placed in position after the wires have been pulled into the conduit, the two parts being held together by screws or other means.

split phase. There are several methods of splitting the phase to start single phase motors, as by providing in addition to the main single phase or running winding. Practically all small single phase induction motors are started by means of a split phase starting winding.

split phase motor characteristics. The torque increases with the speed until the maximum torque point is reached, thus giving rapid acceleration, and insuring that the motor will bring up to speed any load it will start. Adding resistance to the armature not only increases its slip, but also decreases its maximum torque. The power factor is less than the power factor of a polyphase motor of the same speed and rating. The efficiency is lower than for a polyphase motor of the same ratio.

split phase motor starting. In operation when the circuit is closed, the armature starts to revolve upon the shaft; when it reaches a predetermined speed, a centrifugal clutch expands and engages the clutch disc, which is fastened to the shaft. The momentum overcomes the inertia of the driven apparatus. In this it is assisted by a certain amount of slippage in the clutch, which is the case when the armature speed is pulled down to such a point as to reduce the grip of the centrifugal clutch.

spontaneous electricity. A term sometimes applied to the electricity derived from the melting of sulphur.

spot welding. In electric welding, the process of joining or fusing together electrically two or more metal sheets or parts without any preparation of stock.

spring clips. Metal jaws provided with a spring so as to make firm contact with the blades of a knife switch when closed.

spring contact. An electric contact that is actuated by a spring.

spun silk. A coarse, short filament silk tightly twisted. More durable than floss silk.

spurious resistance. The opposition to the flow of alternating current due to inductance. It depends upon the frequency, the shape of the conductor, and nature of the surrounding medium.

square mil. The area of a square whose sides are one mil (.001 inch long) and is equal to .001 x .001 = .000001 square inch. Used for measuring conductors of square or rectangular cross section, such as bus bars, etc.

square wire. A wire having a square cross section, sometimes used in winding armatures.

squirrel cage motor. An asynchronous motor, in which the currents supplied are led through the field coils only, and the armature, not being connected to the external circuit, is rotated by currents induced by the varying field set up through the field coils.

squirrel cage winding. A series of rods or bars having their ends attached to short circuiting rings and forming the armature winding of a squirrel cage motor. In a squirrel cage winding there are a large number of bars uniformly spaced. The name for this form of winding is suggested by the resemblance of the finished armature to the wheel of a squirrel cage.

stack. A rigid assembly of two or more switch and bus insulating units.

staggering. An arrangement of commutator brushes, such that one brush rests upon the commutator surface slightly in advance of the other, so as to bridge over a break in the circuit of the armature wires.

standing pilot. A pilot burner that remains lit after it has been lighted regardless of the system demands. It does not cycle with system demands.

stand off insulator. One attached to a standard so as to hold the conductor it insulates, at a required distance from a building.

star current in polyphase system. In a polyphase system, the current between any terminal and the neutral point, or the current in any branch of the system.

star and delta connections compared. In wiring, the power output of each is the same, but the star connection gives a higher line voltage, so smaller conductors may be used. An objection to the star connection for three-phase work is that it requires the use of three transformers, and if anything happens to one, the entire set is disabled. When three transformers are delta connected, one may be removed and the two remaining units will carry 57.7% of the original three-phase load.

star-delta starting. The process of starting a three-phase motor by connecting it to the supply with the primary winding initially connected in star, then reconnected in delta for running operation.

star drill. A drill bit used in masonry work.

star point. The point where the phases of a three-phase star connected winding join.

starter. An electric controller for accelerating a motor from rest to normal speed and to stop the motor.

starter coil. In magneto ignition, an auxiliary spark producer for furnishing initial spark in starting.

starter, fluorescent lamps. Devices that first connect a fluorescent or similar discharge lamp in a circuit to provide for cathode preheating and then open the circuit so that the starting voltage is applied across the lamp to establish an arc.

starting box. A rheostat for starting a motor.

starting capacitance. The total effective capacitance in series with the auxiliary winding for starting operation.

starting compensator. A device consisting of two or three autotransformers with switches, for supplying an induction motor with low voltage current at starting, and then, as the motor gains in speed, increasing the voltage by steps to that of the line; an auto starter.

starting current. The current passed through the armature and field magnets of a motor at the moment of starting in order to produce the required starting torque.

starting relay. A relay used to direct the electric current to the auxiliary winding in an electric motor during the starting period.

starting torque. The torque exerted by the starting current of a motor to overcome the static friction of the motor at rest.

starting winding. On a split phase motor, a winding placed in slots at 90 electrical degrees from the main winding. The main winding and the starting winding are so proportioned that their respective currents are out of phase, the object being to produce a so-called rotating field. The starting winding usually consists of a relatively small number of turns of fine wire. This gives a high resistance and low reactance and the current is nearly in phase with the applied voltage.

static electricity. A term sometimes applied to the electricity induced and retained in the plates of a condenser or that which is said to reside as a charge upon the surface of a body, as distinguished from dynamic or current electricity.

static relay. A relay or relay unit in which there is no armature or other moving element, the designed response being developed by electronic, solid-state, magnetic, or other components without mechanical motion.

stationary-mounted device. A device that cannot be removed except by the unbolting of connections and mounting supports.

stator. In a dynamo or motor, the part which is fixed, as distinguished from the part which rotates. The fixed part is usually the field and the moving part the rotor or armature.

stay cord. A continuation of the outer braid of a cord, used as a fastening, to relieve the conductors of mechanical strain.

steady current. An electric current of constant amperage.

steam turbine-electric drive. A self-contained system of power generation and application in which the power generated by a steam turbine is transmitted electrically by means of a generator and a motor for propulsion purposes.

Steinmetz's law. A law of hysteresis loss. It states that the loss by hysteresis is proportional to the one and six-tenths power of the induction flux density.

step down transformer. A type used to transform high voltage current into low voltage current for lighting and power circuits. When current is supplied to consumers for lighting purposes and for the operation of motors, etc., considerations of safety as well as those of suitability require lower voltages. Transformers of this type have a large number of turns in the primary winding and a small number in the secondary; the ratio depending on the voltage reduction required.

stepping poles. Poles which require frequent climbing should be provided with steps to prevent damage to the pole from the climbing spurs of the workman. The lowest step is placed not less than 6 1/2' from the ground.

step up transformer. A type used to transform a low voltage current into a high voltage current. Such transformers are employed at the generating end of a transmission line to raise the voltage from the alternator to such value that it will be economical to transmit to a distant point.

stiff field. A magnetic field whose density is comparatively great.

stop. A mechanical or electric device used to limit the excursion of electromechanical equipment.

stopping condenser. One that prevents the flow of DC but permits the flow of AC.

storage battery. A source of electricity made up of a group of storage cells; a secondary, as distinguished from a primary battery.

storage cell. A secondary cell consisting of plates or grids in an electrolyte, of such character that the electrical energy supplied to it is converted into chemical energy (a process called charging). The chemical energy can be reconverted into electrical energy (a process called discharging). The electrolyte generally consists of a weak solution of sulphuric acid which permits ready conduction of the current from the charging source; the greater the proportion of acid within certain limits, the smaller the resistance offered. Properly called the secondary cell.

storm guys. Anchor guys, usually placed at right angles to direction of line, to provide strength to withstand transverse loading due to wind.

story. That portion of a building included between the upper surface of a floor and upper surface of the floor or roof next above.

straight joint. A joint used for connecting two lengths of cable in approximately the same straight line in series.

strain insulator. One used for the double purpose of taking the mechanical strain at a bend or at the end of a conductor and also insulating the same electrically.

strain relief device. Knot, bushing, or equivalent to prevent strain from being transmitted to a wire or cord at a termination point inside fixture.

strand. One of the wires, or groups of wires of any stranded conductor.

stranded wire. A group of small wires used as a single wire. A wire is a slender rod or filament of drawn metal. If such a filament is subdivided into several smaller filaments or strands, and is used as a single wire, it is called a stranded wire. There is no sharp dividing line of size between a stranded wire and a cable. If used as a wire, for example, in winding inductance coils or magnets, it is called a stranded wire and not a cable. If it is substantially insulated, it is called a cord.

strap key. A pushbutton circuit controller that is biased by a spring metal strip and is used for opening or closing a circuit momentarily.

strap switch. A term sometimes used for the simplest form of knife switch, consisting of a blade of copper hinged at one end and making contact at the other end between flexible copper jaws.

stray currents. Currents induced in the mass of a metal either by being cut by a moving magnetic field or by moving in a field. These currents circle about within the metal, absorbing energy and converting it into heat. They are usually called eddy currents. Eddy currents are the cause of much of the lost energy in dynamos, motors, and transformers. To obviate them, iron cores of armatures and induction coils are laminated.

strength of current. The quantity of electricity which flows past any point of the circuit in one second.

strength of magnet. The magnetic force exerted by either of the poles of a magnet.

stress. Force acting upon a solid body by pull, pressure, or in other ways, and which produces distortion or strain.

striking distance. The shortest distance, measured through air, between parts of different polarities.

stringing. In pole line construction, after erecting the poles and equipping them with cross arms, insulators, etc., the process of running the wires from pole to pole.

strip fuse. The simplest form of safety fuse for breaking an electric circuit when the current becomes excessive. It consists of a thin strip of fusible metal provided with copper terminals by which it is screwed down to the terminals of the circuit.

strut. A compression member of a structure.

stud bolt. A bolt with threads on both ends to be screwed into a fixed part at one end and receive a nut upon the other.

studs. Vertically set skeleton members of a partition or wall to which lath is nailed.

subfeeder. Same class as a feeder, but is distinguished either by being one of two or more connecting links between the end of a single feeder and several distributing mains, or by constituting an extension of a feeder.

subharmonic. A wave motion having a frequency lower than the frequency of the fundamental wave; in value equal to the fundamental frequency divided by a whole number.

submains. Electric conductors branching from mains, and themselves serving other branches.

submersible. So constructed as to be successfully operable when submerged in water under specified conditions of pressure and time.

subsidiary conduit. A terminating branch of an underground conduit run, extending from a manhole or handhole to a nearby building, handhole, or pole.

substation system. In electrical distribution by means of transformers, an arrangement in which transformers fed by high pressure currents, are located at advantageous points, having their secondaries joined to a complete network of low-pressure distributing mains.

subtraction. The process of taking one number called the subtrahend from another number called the minuend. The result obtained, or "difference" between the two numbers, is called the remainder.

subtractive and additive polarity. Take a single phase transformer, having two high voltage and two low voltage external terminals, connect one high voltage terminal to the adjacent low voltage terminal and apply voltage across the two high voltage terminals. Then, if the voltage across the unconnected high voltage and low voltage terminals are less than the voltage applied across the high voltage terminals, the polarity is subtractive; while if it is greater than the voltage applied across the high voltage terminals, the polarity is additive.

subway. An underground electric railway used in large cities.

subway-type transformer. A submersible constant current transformer suitable for installation in an underground vault.

summer lightning. Also called heat lightning. A form of lightning flash, seen at the horizon as a sudden lighting up of the clouds without any sound of thunder. It is merely the reflection from a thunder storm at too great a distance for the thunder to be heard.

superposed circuit. An additional circuit obtained from a circuit normally required for another service, and in such a manner that the two services can be given simultaneously without mutual interference.

superconductivity. When metals are cooled to temperatures near absolute zero, most of them become excellent conductors of electricity, with electrons flowing without significant resistance.

supervisory control. A form of remote control, comprising an arrangement for the selective control of remotely located units by electrical means, over one or more common interconnecting channels.

supplementary lighting. Lighting used to provide an additional quantity and quality of illumination that cannot readily be obtained by a general lighting level.

supplement of angle. The difference between a given angle and 180 degrees.

supply mains. In a system of electrical distribution, the mains which convey the current from the central station.

surd. An indicated root that cannot be extracted. A quantity that cannot be expressed in figures.

surface metal raceway. A raceway consisting of an assembly of backing and capping.

surface-mounted device. A device, the entire body of which projects in front of the mounting surface.

surge. A transient wave of current, potential, or power in the electric circuit.

surging. Current variations due to hunting of two alternators working in parallel.

suspension insulator. One which is suspended by a hook or wire.

suspension wire. A wire or cable usually known as messenger wire from which an overhead conductor is suspended.

sweating. A method of soldering in which the surfaces to be joined are cleaned, heated, fluxed, and covered with a film of solder. The soldered surfaces are then placed together and heated, either with a bit or blow torch, until the solder melts and unites the two surfaces. During the heating operation the surfaces should be held firmly together with clamps or other means.

swimming rule. A rule suggested by Ampere for determining the direction of lines of force with relation to that of the current which produces them. It may be stated as follows: Suppose a man is swimming in the wire with the current and that he turns to face a magnetic needle placed near the wire, then the north-seeking pole of the needle will be deflected toward his left hand.

switch. A device for making, breaking, or changing the connections in an electric circuit.

switchblade. The conducting blade of a knife switch by means of which a circuit is closed.

switchboard. A large single panel, frame, or assembly of panels on which are mounted, on the face or back or both, switches, overcurrent and other protective devices, buses, and usually instruments. Switchboards are generally accessible from the rear as well as from the front and are not intended to be installed in cabinets.

switch contacts. Since it is impossible to instantly stop the current by opening the switch, the current continues to flow and momentarily jumps the air gap, resulting in a more or less intense arc which tends to burn the metal of the switch. To partially remedy this, the contact pieces are so shaped that they open along their whole length at the same time, so as to prevent the concentration of the arc at the last point of contact.

switchgear. A general term covering switching and interrupting devices.

switch pin. In a plug switch, the plug or pin which is introduced into the switch hole.

switch stick (hook stick). A stick with an insulated handle and a hook or other means for performing stick operation of a switching device.

symbol for a unit. A letter, a character, or combinations thereof, that may be used in place of the name of the unit.

symmetrical alternating current. A periodic alternating current in which points, one-half a period apart, are equal and have opposite signs.

synchronism. The simultaneous occurrence of any two events. Thus two alternating currents or pressures are said to be "in synchronism" when they have the same frequency and are in phase.

synchronize. To bring two or more alternators into such relation to each other that their pressure waves shall be of equal period and corresponding phase.

synchronous. In unison: In step. Descriptive of two alternating variables having the same frequency and being in phase, for instance, an alternating current in which the voltage is in phase with the current.

synchronous motor. One which rotates in unison or in step with the phase of the alternating current which operates it.

synchronous motor construction. A synchronous motor consists of two elements; (a) an armature; (b) field, either of which may revolve. The field is separately excited with DC. The armature is usually stationary, being attached to the frame, while the field magnets are attached to a frame which revolves with the shaft, the exciting current being delivered through slip-rings.

synchroscope. An instrument used to indicate a difference in frequency between two AC sources.

synchro system. An electrical system that gives remote indications or control by means of self-synchronizing motors.

system ground. The connection between a grounding system and a point of an electric circuit; a neutral point.

system voltage. The root-mean-square, power-frequency voltage from line to line as distinguished from the voltage from line to neutral.

T

T-connector. A connector similar in shape to the letter T and serving to connect a wire with two branch wires.

table lamp. A portable light with a short stand suitable for standing on furniture.

tabulate. To print totals.

tachometer. An instrument for indicating the speed of rotation (rpm).

tails. Induction coil core wires.

talc. A soft silicate of magnesia, also called "soapstone." It is easily split into thin plates, but differs from mica in not possessing elasticity. It is used as heat resisting insulation in spark plugs, etc.

tamper switch. A switch, usually mechanically operated, used to detect opening of alarm equipment boxes.

tandem drive. Two or more drives that are mechanically coupled together.

tangent. A right line touching an arc at one extremity and terminated by a secant passing through the other extremity.

tangent galvanometer. An indicating instrument in which the deflecting coil consists of a coil of wire, within which is placed a needle very short in proportion to the diameter of the coil, and supported at the center of the coil.

tangent scale. The circular scale of a tangent galvanometer, graduated into values of the tangents instead of into equal degrees of arc, in order to obviate the necessity of referring to a table of figures in making computations.

269

tantalum lamp. A form of incandescent lamp having a filament composed of the metal tantalum. As compared with the carbon filament lamp, the tantalum lamp will take much greater current at starting, will reach incandescence more quickly and will be much less sensitive to voltage variation, at the same time consuming less watts with greater candlepower.

tap. In wiring, the connection of the end of one wire to some point along the run of another wire.

taping. Applying a wrapping of insulating tape to a conductor or cable.

tap splicing. The process of uniting the end of one multiwire conductor at some point along the run of another multiwire conductor.

tap switch. A multipoint switch designed for use with a multitap induction coil.

tarnish. Surface discoloration of a metal caused by formation of a thin film of corrosion.

teaser transformer. In three-phase connection with two "T" connected single-phase transformers, the one which is connected between the midpoint of the main transformer and the third wire of the three-phase system.

tee box. In underground cable construction, a junction box resembling the letter "T", for connecting a branch at right angles with a main.

tee connector. A connector shaped like the letter "T" for connecting a wire at right angles with another.

telecommunication. Any transmission or reception of information such as signals, images, writing, or sounds, by electronic means.

telegraph. Electrical apparatus for transmitting messages between distant points.

270

telephone. An instrument for the transmission of articular speech by electric current.

television. Vision obtained of a distant object through a telegraphoscope or instrument involving the use of selenium cells for telegraphically transmitting a picture.

temper. To harden. The process consists in heating the steel to the proper temperature and cooling it.

temperature. That which determines the heat or coldness of anything, the measurement of which is made by the thermometer.

temperature, ambient. Ambient temperature is the temperature of the medium, such as air, water, or earth into which the heat of the equipment is dissipated.

temperature coefficient. The variation of the quantity considered, divided by the difference in temperature producing it.

temperature rise. Current passing through the windings of a motor results in an increase in the motor temperature. The difference between the winding temperature of the motor when running, and ambient temperature, is called the temperature rise. The temperature rise produced at full load is not harmful provided the motor ambient temperature does not exceed 40 degrees C (104 degrees F).

templet. A pattern such as a thin board or paper used as a guide to the form of a piece being made.

temporary ground. A connection between a grounding system and parts of an installation that are normally alive, applied temporarily so that work may be safely carried out in them.

tensile strength. The stress required to produce failure.

tension, electric. Voltage or electric pressure.

terminal. A point at which a connection is made between an electrical apparatus and the external circuit.

terminal block. A terminal block is a rigidly mounted device that is composed of an insulated base with barriers having one or more electrically conductive members. Each electrically conductive member serves as a junction to electrically connect two or more conductors and also provides means to individually connect or disconnect conductors. The device may be a sectional or one-piece design.

terminal board. An insulating base or slab usually mounted in the rear of a switchboard panel, equipped with terminals for connecting the small wiring to the outgoing instrument and control cables, in a convenient and orderly manner.

terminal connector. A connector for attaching a conductor to a lead, terminal block, or stud of electric apparatus.

terminal device. A part used to facilitate the making of one or more electrical connections.

terminal insulator. A line insulator upon a terminal pole.

terminate. To complete an event or stop an operation.

terra cotta. A fired clay; cooked earth. Used for pottery, building material, and architectural ornamentation. Often used in tile.

tertiary. Of 3rd rank, importance, or value; occurring in or being a third stage.

tertiary winding. A third winding on a transformer that is used as a second control winding.

tesla. The tesla is a unit of magnetic induction equal to 1 weber per square meter.

tesla coil. A form of induction coil designed by Tesla for obtaining high voltages and frequencies; it consists of a primary of a few turns of coarse wire and a secondary of fine wire, both immersed in oil insulation; a Tesla transformer.

Tesla, Nikola. An electrical engineer, inventor of the system of polyphase electric currents in 1887. The man that lit up the world.

test. To determine its performance characteristics while functioning under controlled conditions.

tetanus. Persistent spasm of the voluntary muscles. Lockjaw.

therm. A unit of heat; applied especially to gas. One therm = 100,000 B.t.u.

thermal. Relating to heat.

thermal cell. A reserve cell that is activated by the application of heat.

thermal coil. In a rheostat, a coil having a high temperature coefficient introduced for the purpose of indicating the amount of heat generated by the resistance.

thermal cutoff. A temperature or temperature and current-sensitive device, incorporating a thermal element for protecting a circuit by opening the protected circuit when the device reaches a predetermined temperature.

thermal cutout. An overcurrent device that contains a heater element in addition to and affecting a renewable fusible member which opens the circuit. It is not designed to interrupt short-circuit currents.

thermal effect of current. The conductor, along which a current flows, becomes heated. The rise of temperature may be small or great according to circumstances, but some heat is always produced.

thermal element. A metallic or nonmetallic fusible material that is part of a thermal cutoff and is responsive to temperature by a change of state at the temperature for which it is calibrated.

thermally protected. The words "Thermally Protected" appearing on the nameplate of a motor or motor-compressor indicates that the motor is provided with a thermal protector.

thermal protector. A protective device for assembly as an integral part of a motor or motor-compressor and which, when properly applied protects the motor against dangerous overheating due to overload and failure to start. Often referred to as a "heater".

thermal resistance. The opposition made by a body to the flow of heat through it.

thermal unit. A measure of mechanical work, found by experiment to be equal to 1/180 part of the heat required to raise the temperature of one pound of water from 32 degrees to 212 degrees F.

thermistor. A resistor that is used to compensate for temperature variations in a circuit.

thermochrosy. The property of radiant heat which permits its being analyzed into component rays of different refrangibilities, like light rays; heat color.

thermocouple. A device consisting of two electrical conductors having two junctions, one at a point whose temperature is to be measured, and the other at a known temperature. The temperature between the two junctions is determined by the material characteristics and the electrical potential set up.

thermodynamics. The science of the mechanics of heat.

thermoelectric effect. The effect of producing an electric current by unequally heating the junctions of dissimilar metals in a thermocouple.

thermoelectric generator. A device that converts thermal energy into electric energy by direct interaction of a heat flow and the charge carriers in an electric circuit.

thermoelectric laws. The two main laws of thermoelectricity may be stated as follows: (a) The voltage developed by a heated junction depends on the metals used and is independent of the size. (b) If a complete circuit is made of two metals, joined at the extremities, and one junction is heated while the other is kept cold, the voltage generated is proportional to the difference between the temperatures of the hot and cold junction within certain limits.

thermopile. A thermoelectric battery whose operation depends on the fact that if the junction in a circuit, composed of two or more metals, is kept at different temperatures, a current is created in the circuit.

thermopilot relay. A relay whose coil is energized by the electrical power generated by the thermocouple. Its contacts are in the temperature-control circuit from the thermostat.

thermostat. An automatic control actuated by temperature change to maintain temperatures between predetermined limits.

thomson. A name proposed for the mho, the unit of electrical conductance.

threaded coupling. An internally threaded steel cylinder for connecting two sections of rigid steel conduit.

three-phase alternating current. This consists of three alternating currents of equal frequency and amplitude, but differing in phase from each other by one-third of a period.

three-phase circuit. A combination of circuits energized by AC that differ in phase by one-third of a cycle, that is, 120 degrees.

three-phase four-wire system. A three-phase, three-wire system having a fourth wire connected to the neutral point of the source which may be grounded.

three-phase transformer. A combination in one unit of three single-phase transformers with separate electric circuits, but having certain magnetic circuits in common. There are three magnetic circuits through the core, and the fluxes in the various circuits are displaced in phase.

three-way switch. One having three contacts to which external wires are connected, that is, a switch which connects one conductor to either of the other conductors depending on the position of the switch.

three-wire control. A control function that utilizes a momentary-contact pilot device and holding-circuit to provide undervoltage protection.

three-wire system. A system of electrical distribution, employing two dynamos or other current sources joined in series and connected at their free terminals to the positive and negative mains, respectively, between which a neutral wire, usually smaller than the mains, is introduced and joined to the junction of the dynamos.

threshold current. A current magnitude of specified wave shape at which the melting of the current-responsive element (current-limiting fuse) occurs at the first instantaneous peak current for that wave shape.

through bolt. A bolt passing axially through a laminated core, that is used to apply pressure to the end plates of rotating machines.

throw. A term which relates to the extent of the blade movement, with respect to the contact range of a switch.

throw over switch. A knife switch which may be thrown over into either of two opposite sets of contacts; a double throw switch.

thrust bearing. A bearing designed to carry axial load so as to prevent or limit axial movement of a shaft, or to carry the weight of a vertical rotor system.

thumb nut. A nut fitted with projecting wings so that it may be loosened or tightened by hand.

thunder. The report which follows a discharge of lightning, caused by the heat of the air in the region of the flash, producing sudden expansion and compression, followed by a swift burst of air into the rarefied space.

tie feeder. A feeder that connects together two or more independent sources of power and has no tapped load between the terminals.

tie line. A transmission line connecting two or more power systems.

tie wire. In pole line construction, a piece of wire, usually about 16" in length, for tying the line wire to an insulator.

tight. Apparatus is designed as watertight, dust tight, etc., when so constructed that the enclosing case will exclude the specified material under specified conditions.

time clock. A timing device used to control the off and on cycles of equipment in response to the time of day. They have contacts that make and break circuits at a given time each day without personal attention.

time-delay device. Designed to provide a time interval between operations of a device.

time release. A device used to prevent the operation of an operative unit until after the expiration of a predetermined time interval after the device has been actuated.

timing relay. An auxiliary relay or relay unit whose function is to introduce one or more definite time delays in the completion of an associated function.

tin foil. Tin or some alloy resembling tin, rolled into very thin sheets. Tin foil is largely used in making condensers.

tinned cable. A cable having a coating of tin outside of the lead sheath to protect the lead from chemical action in underground work.

tinned wire. Wire covered with tin by the electroplating process.

tin plating. The coating of iron or steel with tin to protect it from oxidation and to provide a bright surface. The iron is first cleaned and then dipped into a bath of melted tin.

tinsel. A very fine, flat, copper ribbon wrapped around a cotton thread.

tip, plug. The contacting member at the end of a plug.

toggle switch. Snap switch, also often called a wall switch.

ton of refrigeration. Refrigeration equivalent to the melting of one ton of ice per 24 hours.

torchere. An indirect floor lamp that sends all or nearly all of its light upward.

torque. The value of the moment of a system which tends to produce rotation. The turning effort or twist which a shaft sustains when transmitting power.

torque motor. A motor designed primarily to exert torque through a limited travel or in a stalled position.

torsion. In mechanics, that force with which a thread, wire, or rod of any material, returns, or tends to return, to a state of rest after being twisted.

totally enclosed motor. A motor which is so completely enclosed by integral or auxiliary covers as to practically prevent the circulation of air through the interior. Such a motor is not necessarily airtight.

track. An enclosure that houses the bus bars and that houses or is integral with the bus bar support. Track is usually made of extruded material that usually resembles an "H" in cross section, with two vertical members connected by a horizontal member.

track circuit. An electric circuit that includes the rails of a track relay as essential parts.

traction motor. An electric propulsion motor used for exerting tractive force through wheels of a vehicle.

transducer. A device operated by power from one system and supplying power in the same or any other form to a secondary system. Either of these systems may, for example, be electrical, mechanical, or acoustical.

transfer box. Also called a "pull box"; a box without a distribution panel containing branched or otherwise interconnected circuits.

transfer device. One which transfers control of breakers, etc., from automatic to test switches, or control of equipment from manual to automatic, automatic to continuous, or performs some transfer operation other than unit sequence.

transfer relay. A circuit opening relay, used where accurate time of operation is required and a separate source of control is not available.

transfer switch. A switch arranged to permit transferring a conductor connection from one circuit to another without interrupting the current.

transformation. The changing of the value of voltage or current by means of a transformer.

transformer. An apparatus used for changing the voltage and current of an alternating circuit. A transformer consists of primary winding, secondary winding, and an iron core. In principle, if a current is passed through a coil of wire encircling a bar of soft iron, the iron will become a magnet; when the current is discontinued the bar loses its magnetization.

279

transformer, isolating. A transformer having electrical insulation and electrostatic shielding between its windings such that it can provide isolation between parts of the system in which it is used.

transformer losses. There are two losses in a transformer; (1) The iron loss or core loss due to hysteresis, eddy currents, or magnetic leakage. (2) The copper losses due to heating the conductors, eddy currents in the conductors, or stray losses.

transformer oil. An insulating and cooling medium used in some types of transformer. The oil should have a low viscosity to flow free at operating temperatures.

transformer, outdoor. A transformer of weatherproof construction.

transformer ratio. The ratio of the number of turns in the primary winding to the number of turns in the secondary windings.

transformer, step-down. A transformer in which the energy transfer is from a high-voltage circuit to a low-voltage circuit.

transformer, step-up. A transformer in which the energy transfer is from a low-voltage circuit to a high-voltage circuit.

transformer vault. An isolated enclosure either above or below ground, with fire-resistant walls, ceiling, and floor, for unattended transformers.

transient. A nonrepetitive or arbitrarily timed electrical surge.

transistor. An active semiconductor device with three or more terminals. Transistors turn on instantly. They don't require a warm-up time like a tube does. A transistor will last for years and very little voltage is needed.

transite. An insulating material used for arc shields.

.

transition relay. One functioning from starting to running which gives an impulse to main circuit devices for changing a machine from the starting to the running connections.

translucence. Partial transparency. Transmitting light, but not permitting objects to be distinctly seen.

transmission, electric. The conveying of electric power from a generating station, by means of transmission circuits, to distant stations where the power is consumed.

transmission line. A line used for electric power transmission.

travel, relay. The amount of movement in either direction towards pickup or reset.

traveling cable. A cable made up of electric conductors that provides electric connection between an elevator or dumbwaiter car and a fixed outlet in the hoistway.

tray. A support or container for one or more battery storage cells.

tree wire. A specially insulated wire designed to resist injury from chafing against a tree.

trega. A prefix to a unit of measurement to denote one trillion times that unit.

trickle charge. The method of charging a storage battery continuously at a very low rate.

trigonometrical functions. A function is a quantity in mathematics, so connected with another quantity, that if any alteration is made in the latter there will be a consequent alteration in the former. The dependent quantity is said to be a function of the other. Thus, the circumference of the circle is a function of the diameter. The trigonometrical functions are certain functions of angles, such as sine, tangent, and secant employed in trigonometry in investigating the relations between the sides and angles of geometric figures.

trigonometry. That branch of mathematics which treats of the measurement of plane and spherical triangles, that is, the determination of three of the parts of such triangles when the numerical values of the other three parts are given.

trimmer. A workman employed to renew the carbons in arc lamps.

trip. Denotes automatic interruption by the ground fault circuit interrupter of the electric circuit to the load.

trip current. The current at which a circuit breaker is intended to open the contact circuit at a given ambient.

trip free relay. A type consisting of a circuit opening auxiliary relay equipped with two coils. One coil, the operating coil, opens the control circuit to the contactor which controls the circuit breaker closing coil, immediately upon the closing of the circuit breaker. The other coil, the holding coil, prevents the relay closing the closing contactor control circuits until the manually operated closing switch is opened. This prevents a circuit breaker being held in a closed position under short circuit conditions and enables the protective relays to trip the circuit breaker even though the manually operated closing switch is held in a closed position.

triphase. In alternating current work, a term sometimes used for three-phase.

triple-pole single-throw switch. A switch which opens or closes three leads by a single throw. It may be the leads of separate circuits or the three leads of a three-wire system.

triple-pole switch. A switch which is provided with three contacts by which it may open and close three electric circuits.

triplex cable. Three insulated single conductors twisted together.

tripping coil. A coil in a circuit breaker which trips or unlocks the spring which controls the contacts, and opens the circuit when the current reaches a definite value.

tripping transformer. One similar in design to the standard class of instrument transformer, but of lower accuracy.

troffer. A long recessed lighting unit usually installed with the opening flush with the ceiling.

troughing. An open earthenware channel, wood, or plastic, in which cables are installed under a protective cover.

trunk feeder. A feeder connecting two generating stations.

trunk-line conduit. A duct bank provided for main or trunk-line cables.

trussed blade. A blade that is reinforced by truss construction to provide stiffness.

trusses. Framed structural pieces consisting of triangles in a single plane for supporting loads over spans.

tubing, EMT. A thin-walled steel raceway of circular form with a corrosion-resistant coating for protection of wires or cables.

tubing, flexible. A mechanical protection for conductors; a flame-resistant and moisture-repellent circular tube of fibrous material.

tungsten. A somewhat rare metal used as a filament in the tungsten incandescent lamp and in vacuum tubes. It is steel gray in color, very heavy, and hard enough to scratch glass. It passes directly into vapor at a very high temperature without entering the liquid state, and has a lower specific resistance than carbon.

tungsten filament. The metal tungsten, being too brittle to be drawn into wire, fine particles of the metal are made into a paste with binding material and squirted through a die. After drying, the particles are welded into a continuous wire.

turbine. A machine in which a rotary motion is obtained by transference of the momentum of a fluid; broadly speaking, the fluid is guided by fixed blades, attached with a casing, and impinging on the other blades mounted on a drum or shaft, causing the latter to revolve.

turbine-driven generator. An electric generator driven by a turbine.

turn. In wire joints, the wrapping of one wire around another wire which remains straight. In rotating machinery, the basic coil element that forms a single conducting loop comprising one insulated conductor.

turnbuckle. A threaded device inserted in a tension member to provide minor adjustment of tension or sag.

turns ratio. In a secondary induction coil, the number of turns in the secondary divided by the number of turns in the primary winding.

twin cable. A cable composed of two insulated stranded conductors laid parallel, having a common covering.

twin conductor. A cable containing two insulated conductors running parallel.

twist. In wire joints, the wrapping of each wire around the other.

twisted cable. A bunched cable in which the conductors are first twisted in pairs, then two pairs are twisted together, a second set of two pairs are then twisted with the first, and so on, for the purpose of eliminating inductive disturbances.

twisted pair. Two small insulated conductors, twisted together, without a common covering. The two conductors of a twisted pair are usually substantially insulated.

two-family dwelling. A building consisting solely of two dwelling units.

two-fer. An adapter cable containing one male plug and two female cord connectors used to connect two loads to one branch circuit.

two-phase alternating current. Two single phase currents flowing in separate circuits but having a phase difference of 90 degrees.

two-phase five-wire system. A system of alternating current supply comprising five conductors, four of which are connected as in a four-wire two-phase system, the fifth being connected to the neutral points of each phase. Although this type of system is usually known as the two-phase five-wire system, it is strictly a four-phase five-wire system.

two-wire circuit. A metallic circuit formed by adjacent conductors insulated from each other.

two-wire system. A system of electrical distribution employed in incandescent lighting in which only two mains are required, as distinguished from the three-wire system in which a third or balance wire is introduced.

tying-in. Fastening an overhead line wire to the insulators by means of the wires.

U

Ufer ground. Years ago tests were conducted in Arizona using 1/2"
steel rebar set in concrete on 24 buildings. The earth resistance readings
proved very low and as a result of these tests the Code accepted Mr.
Ufer's suggestion that a #4 or larger copper wire 20 feet long embedded
in a concrete footing be accepted as an electrode.

ultrasonic frequency. A frequency lying above the audio-frequency
range.

ultraviolet rays. Rays of light existing beyond the violet light of the
visible spectrum, having a more rapid rate of vibration than 800 billion
vibrations per second.

unbalanced circuit. A circuit, the two sides of which are inherently
electrically unlike with respect to a common reference point, usually
ground.

unbalanced polyphase system. A polyphase system of electrical
distribution in which current and phase are unsystematically distributed
through its branches.

uncoated copper. Wire used in the everyday wiring of buildings.
Coated copper is a copper conductor coated with another alloy.

underfloor raceway. A raceway suitable for use in the floor.

underground cable. A cable designed for installation below the
surface of the ground or for installation in an underground duct.

underload relay. A type similar in construction to low voltage relays
but having current instead of pressure windings.

undervoltage protection. The effect of a device, operative on the
reduction of voltage, to cause and maintain the interruption of power to
the main circuit.

undervoltage relay. A relay that operates when the voltage applied to the relay is equal to or less than its setting.

underwriter's knot. A special knot prescribed by the Underwriter's to be made where wires enter a rosette socket or an outlet box, so that the joint will be relieved of any strain due to the weight of the socket, shade, and lamp.

Underwriters' Laboratories. A testing agency whose primary function is to assure that products are manufactured to meet specific safety standards. A listing of a product by the Underwriters' Laboratories indicates that the product was tested and met the recognized safety requirements.

undulating current. An undulatory current. A current whose direction is constant, but whose strength is continuously varying.

undulator. A type of rotating commutator employed on continuous-current circuits for the use of transformers. A commutating device which, from a continuous-current circuit, operates an alternating-current apparatus.

undulatory winding. A wave winding.

ungrounded. A system, circuit, or apparatus without an intentional connection to ground except through potential indicating or measuring devices or other very high impedance devices.

unicoil winding. A concentrated or monotooth armature winding.

unidirectional current. A direct current or a pulsating direct current.

unifilar winding. One having only a single conductor.

uninsulated part. A part that is bare (without insulation) or has insulation that is not in itself acceptable for the operating conditions (such as potential and temperature) involved.

uniphase. Single phase as distinguished from polyphase.

unipolar. Having but one pole, polarity, or direction.

unipolar magnet. A name given to a magnet which, though possessing the necessary two poles, is so suspended that one of the poles lies in the axis of suspension, with the result that the magnet acts as if it possessed only one pole.

unit angle. In circular measure, the angle measured by an arc equal to the radius. It is called the radian.

unit cable construction. That method of cable manufacture in which the pairs of the cable are stranded into groups containing a certain number of pairs and these groups are then stranded together to form the core of the cable.

unit heater. A direct heating, factory made, encased assembly including a heating element, fan, motor, and directional outlet.

unit of capacity. The practical unit of capacity is the farad. A condenser is said to have a capacity of one farad if one coulomb (that is, one ampere flowing one second), when stored on the plates of the condenser will cause a pressure of one volt across its terminals.

unit of current. The practical unit of current is the ampere, which is the current produced by a pressure of one volt in a circuit having a resistance of one ohm.

unit of electric work. The joule.

unit of force. The dyne. It is that force, which by acting upon a mass of one gram during one second, can impart to it an acceleration of one centimeter per second during every second that the force is maintained.

unit of heat. The British thermal unit (B.t.u.) which is 1-180 part of the heat required to raise the temperature of one pound of water from 32 degrees to 212 degrees F.

unit of illumination. The foot-candle, which is the illumination received when one lumen of light falls on one square foot of area.

unit of inductance. The practical unit of inductance is the henry. The induction in a circuit is one henry when the induced pressure is one volt, while the inducing current varies at the rate of one ampere per second.

unit of magnetic flux. The maxwell, which is a single line of magnetic force.

unit of magnetic intensity. The unit value of flux density or intensity is one line or maxwell per square centimeter of the magnetic area. It is called a gauss.

unit of magnetism. That quantity of magnetism which must be concentrated in an infinitely small pole, so that, when placed at a distance of one centimeter from an exactly similar pole, it repels it with a force of one dyne.

unit of magnetomotive force. The gilbert, or that value of magnetic pressure which will establish one line or maxwell per centimeter cube of air.

unit of measure. For scientific purposes, three fundamental units have been fixed which are universally the same. They are the centimeter, the unit of length; the gram, the unit of mass; and the second, the unit of time. This system of units is known as the c.g.s. system, and from these fundamental units other units are derived. (c.g.s. is centimeter, gram, second system).

unit of power. The horsepower or the rate of work done when a weight of 33,000 lbs. is raised one foot in one minute. The watt or 1/746 of a horsepower. It is the power due to a current of one ampere flowing under a pressure of one volt.

unit of pressure. The volt, or pressure which will produce a current of one ampere against a resistance of one ohm.

unit of quantity. The electromagnetic unit is the quantity of electricity which is conveyed by unit current in one second. The practical unit is the coulomb which is the quantity delivered by one ampere flowing for one second.

unit of resistance. The ohm, which is the resistance that permits a flow of one ampere when the impressed pressure is one volt.

unit of self-induction. The henry. The milli-henry or one-thousandth part of a henry is often used as a more convenient unit.

unit of work. The practical unit of electrical energy or work is the joule, which is the work done when one ampere flows for one second against a resistance of one ohm.

units. Established values of physical properties used in measurement and calculation; for example, the volt unit, the ampere unit, and the ohm unit.

unity power factor. This value of the power factor is reached (1.0) when an AC circuit becomes resonant, that is, when the proportion of inductance and capacity are such as to neutralize each other, bring the current in phase with the impressed pressure and causing true watts to equal apparent watts, a condition seldom obtained in practice. An AC circuit has unity power factor when the product of the ammeter and voltmeter readings is equal to the wattmeter reading.

universal joint. A contrivance used for joining two shafts or parts of a machine endwise, so that the one may give a rotary motion to the other when forming an angle with it, or may move freely in all directions with respect to the other.

universal motor. A motor similar to a series DC motor and designed to run on either DC or AC.

unmarked end or pole. The south pole of a magnet, so called to distinguish it from the north pole, which is usually marked for identification.

unplugging. Disconnecting resistance coils from a circuit by withdrawing the plugs of the resistance box.

uranium 235. The nuclear process called fission is obtained by splitting the atom uranium 235.

useful current. In an AC circuit in which the current and voltage are not in phase, that component of the current in phase with the impressed voltage.

utilization equipment. Equipment which utilizes electric energy for mechanical, chemical, heating, lighting, or similar purposes.

utilization factor. The ratio of the maximum demand of a system to the rated capacity of a system.

V

V. Symbol for volt.

vacuum. A space entirely devoid of air or anything which causes pressure; a space having zero absolute pressure.

vacuum envelope. The airtight envelope that contains the electrodes.

vacuum incandescent lamp. One in which the filament is operated in a vacuum.

vacuum lightning arrester. A lightning arrester consisting of a vacuum tube of glass through which a lightning discharge may be grounded.

vacuum switch. A switch whose contacts are enclosed in an evacuated bulb, usually to minimize sparking.

valance. Mounted across the top of a window or along a wall, used to conceal light sources, giving both upward and downward distributions.

valve. A device for opening or closing a pipe, to allow or prevent the flow of a liquid or gas.

vapor. Moisture in the air; any light cloudy substance in the air, as smoke or fumes.

vaportight. So enclosed that vapor will not enter the enclosure.

vars. Reactive volt-amperes.

variable. A quantity or condition that is subject to change.

variable ratio transformer. One with a tapped winding permitting the ratio between primary and secondary to be varied in steps.

292

variable resistance. A resistor whose resistance may be varied while in operation; as a rheostat.

variable-speed device. An electric drive so designed that the speed varies through a considerable range as a function of load.

variolosser. A device whose loss can be controlled by voltage or a current.

varlometer. An instrument employed to determine the relative values of the horizontal component of the earth's magnetic field in different places.

varmeter. An instrument for measuring reactive power.

varnish. An insulating varnish is prepared for coating electric coils, which is claimed to be flexible, acid, salt and moisture-proof, not blistering under heat, and possessed of high insulating properties.

varying duty. Operation of loads, and for intervals of time, both of which may be subjected to wide variation.

varying speed motor. A motor in which the speed varies with the load, ordinarily decreasing as the load increases; for example, a series motor, compound motor, or series shunt motor.

vault. A room constructed of iron, steel, brick, concrete, stone, tile, or similar masonry units, permanently built into or assembled on the premises and having an iron or steel, or equivalent, door and frame with a combination lock.

vector. Any quantity which has direction as well as magnitude. Motion, displacement, velocity, acceleration, force, electric current, magnetic flux, lines of force, stresses and strains, flow of heat and fluids; all involve magnitude and direction and are vector quantities.

vector diagram. Straight lines of definite length may be used to represent vector quantities, the length of the line representing the magnitude, and the inclination of the line to some axis representation of this kind is called a vector diagram.

vector quantity. Any physical quantity whose specification involves both magnitude and direction and that obeys the parallelogram law of addition.

vector sum. The geometrical sum of two or more vector quantities.

velocity. Rate of motion. The relation of motion to time, measured by the number of units of space passed over by the moving body in a unit of time; usually the number of feet in a second.

vent. An opening in rotating machinery that will permit the flow of air.

ventilated. Provided with a means to permit circulation of air sufficient to remove an excess of heat, fumes, or vapors.

ventilating fan. A blowing machine, either of rotary or centrifugal type, used for ventilation.

ventilation ducts. In large armatures, ducts or passages for ventilation to carry off the heat are provided in the core by occasionally separating the discs by the insertion of blocks of insulating materials.

vernier. A short scale made to slide along the divisions of a graduated instrument for indicating parts of divisions, as the limb of a sextant or the scale of a barometer.

vernier control. A method for improving resolution.

vertical. Upright or perpendicular to a horizontal line or plane. Vertical and perpendicular are not synonymous terms.

vertical-break switch. A switch in which the travel of the blade is in a plane perpendicular to the plane of the mounting base.

vertical conductor. A wire or cable extending in an approximately vertical direction on the supporting pole or structure.

vertical riser cable. Cable designed for use in long vertical runs, as in high-rise buildings.

vibrating bell. A bell having a mechanism designed to strike repeatedly, when and as long as actuated.

vibration. Quick motion to and fro. Oscillation as of a pendulum or musical cord.

vibrator. A spring-mounted tongue or blade which is actuated by the magnet of an induction coil, and by its vibration rapidly makes and breaks the primary circuit, resulting in inductive action in the secondary of the coil.

vibrator coil. A secondary coil used in high-tension ignition having a vibrator connected in series in the primary circuit so as to give a series of sparks for each ignition instead of only one.

virgin iron. A term applied to iron that has never been magnetized.

virtual resistance. In an AC circuit, the impedance, which is the ratio of the impressed voltage to the current. It is that quantity which, when multiplied by the current, gives the impressed voltage. It is equal to the square-root of the sum of the squares of the resistance and reactance, and is measured in ohms.

viscosity. The property of a fluid to resist flow or change of shape.

visibility. The quality of state of being perceivable by the eye.

visual angle. An angle formed by the intersection of two lines conceived to be drawn from the extremities of an object to the center of the eye.

vis-viva. The kinetic energy of a moving body. Mechanical energy.

vitreous. Consisting of glass; of, pertaining to, or derived from glass.

vitreous electricity. A term applied to the electricity developed in a glass rod by rubbing it with silk.

vitrified clay. A clay which has been subjected to intense heat so as to receive a glassy surface which renders it absolutely proof against chemical action. It has very high insulating properties which makes it very valuable for conduits in underground wiring.

vitrified clay conduit. It consists of troughs either simple or with partitions.

vitrite. A hard and infusible variety of glass useful for insulating purposes in electrical apparatus.

volatile flammable liquid. A flammable liquid having a flash-point 100 degrees F or whose temperature is above its flash-point.

volatilization, electric. The reduction of a substance to vapor through extreme electrical heat.

volt. The practical unit of electric pressure. The pressure which will produce a current of one ampere against a resistance of one ohm.

volta effect. If two dissimilar metals are placed in contact and then quickly separated, an electric current will flow from one to the other. The effect is greatly increased by submerging both metals in a saline solution.

voltage (of a circuit). The greatest root-mean-square (effective) difference of potential between any two conductors of the circuit concerned.

voltage buildup. The inherent establishment of the excitation current and induced voltage of a generator.

voltage divider. A device for obtaining a desired voltage. It consists of an adjustable slide resistance so arranged, that by shifting the slide contact, any fraction of the voltage impressed on its fixed end terminals may be obtained.

voltage drop. The drop of pressure in an electric circuit due to the resistance of the conductor. This loss exists in every circuit. It is directly proportional to the length of the conductor, and is inversely proportional to its area of cross-section.

voltage limit. A control function that prevents a voltage from exceeding prescribed limits.

voltage, nominal. A nominal value assigned to a circuit or system for the purpose of conveniently designating its voltage class (as 120/240, 480Y/277, 600). The actual voltage at which a circuit operates can vary from the nominal within a range that permits satisfactory operation of equipment.

voltage regulator. An induction device having one or more windings in shunt with, and excited from, the primary circuit, and having one or more windings in series between the primary circuit and the regulated circuit.

voltage relay. One which functions at a predetermined value of voltage. A voltage relay may be either an over-voltage relay or an under-voltage relay.

voltage spread. The difference between maximum and minimum voltages.

voltage taps. On a transformer, leads brought out at various points from one of the windings to obtain various winding ratios corresponding to the voltages desired.

voltage to ground. For grounded circuits, the voltage between the given conductor and that point or conductor of the circuit that is grounded; for ungrounded circuits, the greatest voltage between the given conductor and any other conductor of the circuit.

voltaic. A term formerly applied to electric phenomena produced by the current from primary batteries.

voltaic battery. An electric battery composed of a primary cell or cells.

voltaic cell. In its simplest form, a vessel containing a liquid called the electrolyte, into which two dissimilar metals, called electrodes, are immersed, upon one of which the liquid exerts chemical action, so that an electric current is set-up through a circuit formed by a metallic contact between the electrodes by means of an external condition. Preferably called a primary cell.

voltaic effect. The effect of current to result from the contact of two dissimilar metals under certain conditions.

volt-ampere. The volt-ampere is the apparent power in an AC circuit.

voltmeter. An instrument of high resistance for measuring differences of pressures in volts.

V-O-M meter. Volt-ohm-milliammeter, the troubleshooters' basic testing instrument.

vulcanite. A hard compound produced by heating rubber to a high temperature and mixing it with sulphur.

vulcabeston. An insulating material composed of rubber and asbestos.

W

W. Symbol for wattage.

wall bracket. A lamp bracket attached to a wall.

wall bushing. A bushing intended primarily to carry a circuit through a wall or other grounded barrier.

wall plug. A plug designed to be introduced into a wall socket for the purpose of making electrical connection with the supply wires.

wall socket. Any socket placed in a wall for the purpose of admitting a plug for making electrical connection with supply wires.

warp switch. A thermal relay switch actuated by the heating effect of an electric current.

washer. A ring of metal, leather, or other material, used to relieve friction, to secure tightness of joints or for other purposes.

waste magnetic field. A stray field.

water as a conductor. Water is a conductor, though of an order greatly inferior to the metals. The atmosphere contains, suspended in it, always more or less aqueous vapor, the presence of which impairs its insulating property.

water cooled. A term applied to apparatus cooled by circulating water, the water or water ducts coming in direct contact with major parts of the apparatus.

water heater. An appliance for supplying hot water for domestic or commercial purposes other than for space heating.

water heater, booster. A water heater furnishing hot water from initially heated water, that is usually 60 degrees C (140 degrees F), with the minimum output water temperature being 77 degrees C (170 degrees F).

waterproof. So constructed or protected that moisture will not interfere with its successful operation.

waterproof enclosure. An enclosure so constructed that any moisture or water leakage that may occur into the enclosure will not interfere with its successful operation.

water pyrometer. A pyrometer which determines the temperature of a furnace or other source of intense heat by exposing a metal cylinder of a specified weight to the source of heat for a specified time and then placing the cylinder into a known weight of water and noting the increase of temperature in the water.

watertight. So constructed that moisture will not enter the enclosure under specified test conditions.

watt. The practical unit of power, being the amount of energy expended per second by an unvarying current of one ampere under a pressure of one volt.

wattage. In incandescent electric lighting, the number of watts of electric current consumed by a lamp in order to provide a given candlepower of light. The commercial term is watts per candle.

watt-hour. A unit of electrical work, equal to a rate of one watt expended for one hour. The watt-hour represents the amount of work done by an electric current of one ampere strength flowing for one hour under a pressure of one volt.

watt-hour meter. A meter that will register the watt-hours expended during a period of time.

wattless component. In an alternating current, a component of the current in quadrature with the volts so that it fails to contribute to the energy of the current; the idle component as distinguished from the active component.

wattless current. An alternating current that can do no useful work. The condition at zero power factor. The term wattless current, as understood, does not indicate an absence of electrical energy in the circuit; its elements are there, but not in an available form for external work. The false power due to the so-called wattless current, pulsates in and out of the circuit without accomplishing any useful work.

wattmeter. An electrical instrument designed to measure directly the products of the amperes and volts in a circuit and give its readings in watts.

wave. The variation of current, potential, or power at any point in the electric circuit.

way. The throw of a switch. Thus, a three-throw switch is one in which a connection can be made through the center contact with any one of three circuits.

weatherproof. So constructed or protected that exposure to the weather will not interfere with successful operation.

web. Central portion of an I-beam.

weber. The unit of magnetic flux.

weep hole. A small hole left for draining through the masonry of a retaining wall.

welding. Uniting metals at a high temperature and leaving no trace of a junction.

welding, electric. Welding by the use of heat electrically generated.

welder, electric. An apparatus for welding metals by electricity. A typical welder consists of a self-excited dynamo, a self-adjusting stabilizing reactor which automatically steadies the arc under all welding conditions, making the arc easy to start and maintain.

western union wire joint. A simple method of joining the ends of two wires so as to be mechanically strong and preserve electric conductivity. It consists in overlapping the ends of the bare wire for a few inches, and then twisting each end around the other wire for a few turns. It is also called the American twist joint.

wet contact. A contact through which direct current flows.

wet location. Installations underground or in concrete slabs or masonry, in direct contact with the earth, and locations subject to saturation with water or other liquids, such as vehicle washing areas, and unprotected locations exposed to the weather.

wet-wound. A coil in which the conductors are coated with wet resin in passage to the winding form, or on to which a bonding or insulating resin is applied to produce an impregnated coil.

Wheatstone bridge method. The Christie (erroneously called Wheatstone) bridge is almost universally used for accurate measurements of resistance, which are determined by the proportion existing between the resistances of the arms of the bridge. The resistance of one of them can be calculated when the resistances of the other three are known.

whip. A name sometimes given to a vibrating contact.

whipping. Tie string or tie wire wound around the end of a rope to prevent unraveling.

whirls, electric. The circular lines of force which are conceived to surround a conductor carrying an electric current.

white brass. An alloy of copper and zinc, with sufficient of the latter, or of nickle, lead, etc., to give it a white color. Also called white nickle brass.

white heat. An intense heat which causes a substance to become incandescent and emit a white light.

whole coil winding. An armature winding in which there is one coil per phase per pole; the whole (every one) of the poles being subtended by coils.

wicking. The flow of solder along the strands and under insulation of stranded lead wires.

wind bracing. A system of bracing for securing the position of conductors or their supports to avoid the possibility of contact due to deflection by wind forces.

wind, electric. At the tip of a charged pointed conductor, the density becomes so great that the air surrounding the point becomes electrified by contact and is at once repelled. Unelectrified air takes its place and is repelled in turn. This goes on until so much electricity is carried away from the conductor that not enough remains to electrify the air. During the discharge an electric wind or convection steam blows from the point. It is caused by the stream of ions communicating its momentum to the air.

winding. An assembly of coils designed to act in consort to produce a magnetic flux field or to link a flux field.

winding diagram. A method of representing by means of a diagram, the relations of windings as they actually appear upon the armature. Different colors are often used for indicating the different circuits or phases in the winding.

window contact. An electric contact which rings an alarm upon the opening of a window, or upon any tampering with a window, in an effort to effect an entrance by it.

windup. Lost motion in a mechanical system that is proportional to the force or torque applied.

wiper. An electrical contact arm.

wiping contact. An electric contact made by the brushing of one conductor past another.

wire. A slender rod or filament of drawn metal. The definition restricts the term to what would ordinarily be understood by the term "solid wire." In the definition, the word "slender" is used in the sense that the length is great in comparison with the diameter. If a wire is covered with insulation, it is properly called an insulated wire; while primarily the term "wire" refers to the metal. Nevertheless, when the context shows that the wire is insulated, the term "wire" will be understood to include the insulation.

wire-binding screw. A screw used as a post around which a wire is terminated.

wire-binding screw connector. A connector that uses a screw for holding a conductor and in which the conductor is wrapped under the head of the screw.

wire connector, screw tightening pressure. A device that establishes the connection between two or more conductors or between one or more conductors and a terminal by tightening a screw, except for a wire-binding screw or stud and nut type.

wire connector, separable type. Connections consisting of separable, mating members that can be readily engaged or disengaged without the use of tools.

wire drum. In overhead wire construction, a drum or sheave upon which the wire is wound ready for paying-out.

wire gauge. A gauge for measuring the diameter of round wire according to an arbitrary standard.

wire joint. Any means of uniting the ends of two wires, as the American twist or the Britannia joint, etc.

wire mold. A multioutlet assembly.

wire nut. Laymans' term for a commonly used type of solderless connector.

wireway. A sheet-metal duct (usually U-shaped trough with a hinged or removable cover) in which insulated wires are to be laid in place after the duct system has been completely installed.

wiring. In electrical work, putting in place and connecting the various conductors of lighting and power circuits.

wiring, internal. Wiring and electrical connections that are made within the apparatus by the manufacturer. Within racks or panels, interconnections between separate pieces of apparatus made in accordance with detailed instructions from the apparatus manufacturer are considered to be internal wiring.

wiring under floors. A typical underfloor system consists of a network of rectangular steel ducts, single or multiple, imbedded in the floor.

wiring under plaster. For underplaster extensions, such extensions shall be run in rigid or flexible conduit, armored cable, electrical metallic tubing of approved standard types.

withstand test voltage. The voltage that the device must withstand without flashover, disruptive discharge, puncture, or other failure when voltage is applied under specified conditions.

wolfram. A name sometimes given to tungsten; a somewhat rare metal employed for the filament in the tungsten incandescent lamp.

wollaston wire. Platinum wire drawn very fine.

work. The product of force by the distance through which the force acts; work is numerically equal to energy.

working value. The electrical value that when applied to an electromagnetic instrument causes the member to move to its fully-energized position.

working voltage. Also termed "closed-circuit voltage"; the terminal voltage of a source of electricity under a specified current demand; the rated voltage of an electrical component such as a capacitor.

workmanlike manner. Electric equipment shall be installed in a neat and workmanlike manner; characteristic of a skilled workman or craftsman.

wormgeared machine. A direct-drive machine in which the energy from the motor is transmitted to the driving sheave or drum through worm gearing.

wound rotor. The armature winding of an external resistance or slip-ring induction motor. The winding is polyphase similar to the field winding, and is connected at one end and brought out to a variable external resistance through slip-rings.

wrapped wire. A conductor wrapped in an insulating cover.

X

X. Symbol for reactance.

X-ray. An electromagnetic radiation with extremely short wavelength, capable of penetrating solid substances; used in industrial plants to check the perfection of device and component fabrication (detection of flaws).

X-ray transformer. A transformer serving to obtain the high potential discharges used in X-ray tubes.

X-rays. A curious kind of radiation discovered by and named after Roentgen, the exact nature of which is not yet known. Rays which readily penetrate and pass through diverse substances; causing fluorescence in certain bodies and producing on photographic plates an actinic effect; causing the discharge of an insulated charged conductor, and producing a troublesome affection of the skin when exposed to the rays too long.

Y

Y connection. This method of transformer connection consists in connecting both the primaries and secondaries in star grouping.

Y joint. A branch-joint used to connect a conductor to a main conductor or cable for providing a branched current path.

Y section. Also termed "T section"; an arrangement of three resistors, reactors, or impedances which are connected together at one end of each, with their other ends connected to individual circuits.

yoke. In certain forms of electromagnets, having two straight cores, a piece of soft iron screwed to the cores yoking them together.

yoke (equipment). The yoke is the mounting strap of a device. Each yoke is calculated at 180va.

Z

Z. Symbol for impedance.

zero. Cipher; nothing; naught; the point from which the graduation of a scale, as of a thermometer, commences.

zero, absolute, of temperature. The temperature at which a body has no heat in it (-459.6 degrees F or -273.1 degrees C).

zero adjuster. A machine screw provided under the window of a meter for bringing the pointer exactly to the zero mark on the scale.

zero power factor. A value of the power factor which corresponds to a phase difference between current and voltage of 90 degrees.

zero voltage level. A horizontal line drawn through a wave-form to indicate where the positive excursion falls to zero value, followed by the negative excursion. In a sine-wave, the zero voltage level is located halfway between the positive peak and the negative peak.

zigzag lightning. A form of lightning flash which follows a zigzag path. It is also called forked lightning when it splits up into branches.

zinc. A white metal with a faint bluish tinge. It is used in making galvanized iron, and in the preparation of many alloys such as brass, bronze, and German silver. It forms the negative pole of nearly all primary cells.

zip cord. Any parallel construction wire, usually two or three conductor and #16 gauge or smaller.

PRONUNCIATION

Acetate (ASS-it-tate)
Alkali (AL-kuh-lie)
Alkaline (AL-kah-lin)
Aluminum (ah-LUU-min-um)
Ambient (AM-bee-ant)
Ammeter (AM-meet-er)
Ampere (AM-peer)
Amplitude (Am-pla-tude)
Analog (AN-ah-log)
Analysis (a-NAL-e-sis)
Anode (AN-ode)
Armature (ARM-ah-cher)
Atom (AT-tum)
Cadmium (CAD-mee-um)
Calculations (cal-cue-LAY-shunz)
Cambric (CAM-brick)
Capacities (ka-PASS-it-teez)
Capacitors (ca-PASS-it-erz)
Celcius (SELL-see-us)
Cellulose (CELL-you-lohs)
Centimeters (SENT-ah-mee-terz)
Centrifugally (sen-TRIF-a-gul-lee)
Ceramic (sir-RAM-mik)
Chassis (CHASS-see)
Chemical (KEM-ick-ul)
Circuit (SIR-kit)
Coefficient (co-e-FISH-unt)
Coercive (co-ER-sive)
Commutator (KOM-you-tate-er)
Components (come-POE-nents)
Concentric (kon-SENT-trick)
Condensor (con-DEN-sir)
Conductance (con-DUCK-tants)
Conductivity (con-duck-TIV-it-tee)
Conductor (kon-DUCK-tor)
Constant (CON-stunt)
Consumed (kun-SOOMD)

Continuity (KON-tin-YOU-it-tee)
Conversely (con-VERS-lee)
Corona (kor-OWN-ah)
Corrosive (kor-ROW-siv)
Coulomb (CUU-lome)
Crystalline (KRIS-tall-in)
Cycle (SIY-kul)
Cylindrical (se-LIND-ri-kel)
D'Arsonval (DAR-sun-val)
Deenergize (de-EN-er-jize)
Density (DEN-city)
Depiction (dee-PICK-shun)
Deterioration (dee-TEER-ee-or-AY-shun)
Diamagnetic (DIE-a-mag-NET-ick)
Dielectric (die-ee-LECK-trick)
Dioxide (die-OX-eyed)
Dissipated (DIS-ah-pate-ed)
Dissipation (dis-i-PAY-shun)
Distribution (dis-trib-BUU-shun)
Domain (Do-MANE)
Ductile (DUCK-til)
Electrodes (ee-LECK-trodz)
Electrolyte (ee-LEK-trow-lite)
Electromotive (e-LECK-tro-MO-tiv)
Electrons (ee-LECK-trahns)
Electrostatic (ee-LECK-tro-STAT-tick)
Elliptical (ee-LIP-ti-cul)
Equilibrium (EE-kwal-LIB-ree-umm)
Equivalent (ee-KWIV-ah-lent)
Farad (FAIR-ud)
Ferromagnetic (FAIR-o-mag-NET-ick)
Ferrules (FAIR-ulz)
Fluctuates (FLUK-chew-ates)
Flux (Flucks)
Frequency (FREE-kwin-see)
Galvanic (gal-VAN-ic)
Galvanometer (gal-van-AHM-meter)

Hertz (HURTS)
Hydrometer (high-DRAH-met-er)
Hydroxide (high-DROX-eyed)
Hypotenuse (high-POT-ah-nus)
Hysteresis (hiss-tur-REE-sis)
Impedance (im-PEE-duns)
Impregnated (im-PREG-nate-ted)
Improvise (IM-pro-vise)
Incandescence (in-can-DESS-ants)
Induction (in-DUCK-shun)
Inertia (in-ER-sha)
Infinite (IN-fin-it)
Infinity (in-FIN-it-tee)
Inherent (in-HAIR-ent)
Intense (in-TENTS)
Interference (in-ter-FEAR-ants)
Inversely (in-VERSE-lee)
Ionized (EYE-ahn-ized)
Ions (EYE-onz)
Joules (JEW-elz)
Junction (JUNK-shun)
Kilowatt (KILL-o-wat)
Kirchhoff (KER-choff)
Laminated (LAM-in-ate-ed)
Linear (LIN-ee-er)
Magnitude (MAG-nit-tuud)
Manganese (MANG-gan-neez)
Megawatt (MEG-ah-wat)
Mica (MY-cuh)
Microfarads (MY-kro-FAIR-uds)
Milliamperes (MILL-ee-am-perz)
Molecule (MOL -i-kuul)
Negative (NEG-ah-tiv)

Neutralize (NEW-tral-eyes)
Neutrons (NEW-trahns)
Nichrome (NYE-krohm)
Nonmetallic (non-met-AL-ick)
Nucleus (NEW-klee-us)
Ohmmeter (OHM-meet-er)
Orifice (OR-ih-fiss)
Oxidized (OX-ah-dyzd)
Parallel (PAIR-a-lel)
Paramagnetic (PAIR-a-mag-NET-ick)
Permeability (per-me-a-BILL-it-tee)
Permeable (PERM-me-ah-bul)
Permeance (PER-me-unse)
Peroxide (per-OX-ide)
Perpendicular (PERR-penn-DICK-you-lar)
Photoelectricity (FOE-toe-ee-leck-TRIS-city)
Picofarad (PEE-ko-FAIR-ud)
Piezoelectric (PEE-zo-ee-LECK-trick)
Piezoelectricity (PEE-zo-ee-leck-TRIS-city)
Pneumatic (new-MAT-ick)
Polarities (pole-AIR-it-tees)
Polarity (po-LAIR-it-tee)
Polarization (POLE-er-eye-ZAY-shun)
Polyphase (PA-lee-faze)
Polystyrene (polly-STY-reen)
Porosity (pour-AH-sit-ee)
Potassium (po-TAS-ee-um)
Potential (po-TEN-shul)
Potentiometer (po-TENT-she-AHM-it-er)
Proportionately (pro-POUR-shun-at-lee)
Protons (PRO-tahns)
Pythagorean (pith-THAG-oh-REE-un)
Radians (RAY-dee-uns)
Ratio (RAY-she-oh)
Reactance (ree-AK-tuns)
Receptacle (ree-SEP-tick-al)
Reciprocal (ree-SIP-row-kal)

Reciprocating (ree-SIP-row-kate-ing)
Rectifier (RECK-ta-fy-er)
Rectify (RECK-tih-fye)
Relative (RELL-ah-tive)
Reluctance (ree-LUK-tunse)
Repel (ree-PEL)
Repulsion (ree-PUL -shun)
Residual (re-ZID-u-al)
Resistance (re-ZIS-tents)
Resonance (REZ-uh-nunce)
Resultant (ree-ZUL-tent)
Retentivity (ree-ten-TIV-i-tee)
Rotor (ROTE-ur)
Salient (SAY-lee-ent)
Schematic (ski-MAT-tic)
Secondary (SEK-un-dare-ee)
Sediment (SED-i-ment)
Semiconductors (SEM-ee-kon-DUCK-terz)
Silicon (SILL-ih-kon)
Simultaneously (sy-mul-TAY-nee-us-lee)
Sinusoidal (SINE-yu-SOY-dul)
Solenoid (SOLE-en-noyed)
Solidified (sol-LID-if-eyed)
Stator (STATE-ur)
Sulfating (SUL-fate-ing)
Symmetrically (sim-MET-trick-lee)
Synchronized (SINK-row-nyzd)
Synchronizes (SINK-row-nize-ehs)
Synchronous (SINK-row-nus)
Synchroscope (SINK-row-skope)
Synthetic (sin-THET-tick)
Syringe (sir-INJ)
Tangent (TANN-jent)
Tensile (TEN-sul)
Terminals (TERM-in-nals)
Theorem (THEAR-um)
Thermocouple (THER-moe-kup-pul)

315

Thermoelectricity (THER-moe-ee-leck-TRIS-city)
Thermostatically (ther-mist-STAT-ick-lee)
Torque (TORK)
Transient (TRAN-see-ent)
Transposed (trance-POZD)
Triangulation (try-ang-you-LAY-shun)
Vector (VEK-tur)
Voltaic (vohl-TAY-ick)
Voltmeter (VOLT-meet-er)
Wattage (WAT-edge)

FIRE FACTS

CHEMISTRY OF FIRE

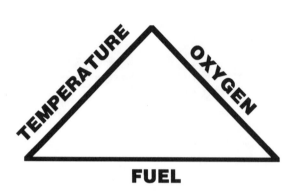

To have a fire, you must have three things present: Fuel, oxygen, and heat. Take away any one of those three and the fire will be extinguished.

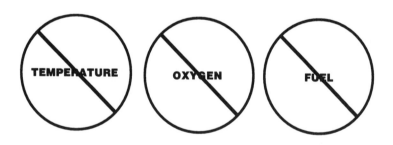

IGNITION TEMPERATURES OF SOLIDS

Wood and Fibrous Materials:

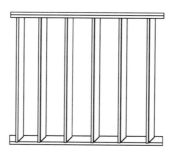

Material	Type of Speciman	Degrees F
Pine	shavings	442°
Douglas Fir	shavings	500°
White Pine	shavings	507°
Newspaper	cuts	446°
Cotton sheeting	roll	464°
Woolen Blankets	roll	536°
Rayon	roll	536°
Nylon	roll	887°
Wood Fiber Board	piece	421-444°
Tin Fiber Board	piece	464°
Black rubber	buffings	374°
Matches	heads	325°
Shellac	scales	810°
Paint film, Varnish	powder	864°

100
watt
A-19

Shown below are the surface temperatures of a 100 watt A-19 lamp in various positions.

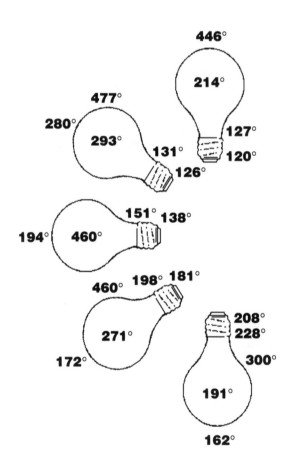

320

FIRE GLOSARY

accelerant. Normally considered a flammable liquid such as gasoline or kerosene but may consist of anything flammable, such as newspapers, wood shavings, etc.

alligatoring. Char patterns formed on burning wood.

arson. The crime of purposely setting fire to another's building or property or to one's own as to collect insurance. It should be noted that various states have defined arson within their laws and statutes.

auto-ignition temperature. The temperature to which a substance must be raised to vapors to ignite spontaneously without the presence of an independent heat source.

boiling point. The boiling point of liquid is the temperature at which the liquid becomes vapor.

depth of char. The depth of the pyrolyzed (or charred) wood surface.

explosive or flammable limits. In the case of flammable liquids, the concentration of vapor necessary when mixed with oxygen that will explode when ignition is applied. Concentrations below and above these limits are not explosive or flammable.

fire. The rapid oxidation of a substance.

fire load. The amount of combustible material per square foot contained in a room or building. It should be noted that the rate of burning and progress of the fire will be influenced by the contents of the room.

fire point. The lowest temperature at which vapors are burning at the same rate that they are generated. The temperature is high enough to support continuous combustion and will be from 10-50° F. above the flash point of the material.

flashover. The rapid involvement of combustible material in a room due to the gradual rising of temperatures to the ignition point simultaneously by either radiation, convection or conduction or a combination of all three, usually when room temperature reaches 600-700°F.

flash point. After a solid or liquid is heated sufficiently to give off vapors capable of ignition, the flash point is the temperature at which the application of heat will cause this vapor to ignite. NOTE: It is the minimum temperature which will ignite the vapor. It is NOT the temperature at which the vapor will sustain burning.

ignition temperature. The temperature of a substance that is the minimum temperature needed to cause self-sustaining combustion of the substance.

kindling temperature. Another term for ignition temperature but is normally applied to the ignition of wood. It is the temperature to which the wood must be raised to be ignited and sustain combustion.

melting point. The temperature at which a substance changes from a solid to a liquid.

pyrolysis. The destruction of wood through the application of heat in the presence or absense of oxygen.

spalling. The breakdown in tensile strength of concrete. This is usually accompanied by a color change and is caused by the application of high heat temperature which causes the trapped moisture in the concrete to expand.

trailers. Any combustible material used to spread a fire from one area of a building to another. Usually a liquid accelerant such as gasoline, but can be material such as newspapers, sawdust, etc.

"V" pattern. The pattern formed on combustible material by fire is usually "V" shaped. This is due to the fact that fire characteristically burns vertically, spreading slightly horizontally. The low point of the "V" pattern is usually the point of fire origin, however, type of material, ventilation and obstacles can affect the formation and final pattern.

FORMULAS

Watt

Ampere

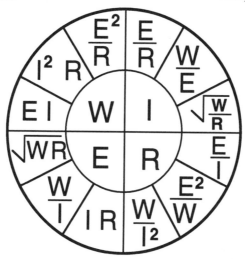

Volta

Ohm

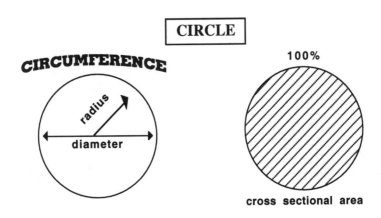

Circumference = The distance around the circle.

Diameter = The distance across a circle through the center.

Radius = The distance from the center to the edge of a circle.

Cross sectional area = 100% of the circle.

The ratio of the circumference to the diameter of a circle is called Pi π = 3.1416. An approximate fraction is 22/7.

Circumference of a circle = Diameter x 3.1416
$\qquad\qquad\qquad\qquad$ Radius x 6.283185

Example: What is the circumference of a 3" circle? 3" x 3.1416 = **9.4248"**

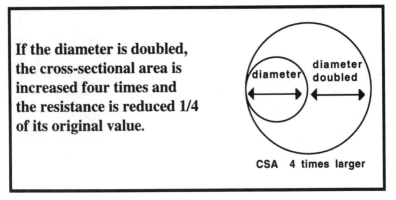

If the diameter is doubled, the cross-sectional area is increased four times and the resistance is reduced 1/4 of its original value.

1 mil = .001 inch
1 inch = 1000 mils
mils = inches x 1000
inches = mils x .001
square inches = square mils x .000001
1 circular mil = 0.7854 square mils
1 square mil = 1.2732 circular mils
circular mils = square mils x 1.2732
square mils = circular mils x 0.7854

1 circular mil = .7854 square mils
You can remember this by reading your
calculator starting at the top left with "**7**",
the number to the right of 7 is "**8**" and
below 8 is "**5**" and to the left of 5 is "**4**". By
reading this box in a clockwise direction
you will remember **7854**.

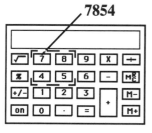

 Bus Bar Square inch area =   Width x Thickness

**Ampacity =   1000 amps per square inch for copper
700 amps per square inch for aluminum**

AREA OF SQUARE INCH

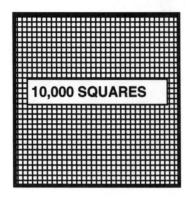

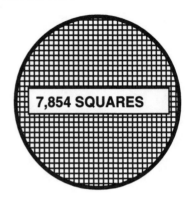

The diagram above illustrates why the decimal .7854 is used to find the area of a circle. If the square is divided into 10,000 small squares, a circle would contain 7,854 small squares. If the area of the square was 1 sq.in., then the area for the circle would be 1" x 1" x .7854 = .7854 square inches for the circle.

$$\textbf{AREA SQ.IN.} = \textbf{D}^2 \textbf{ x .7854}$$
$$\textbf{AREA SQ.IN.} = \textbf{RADIUS}^2 \textbf{ x 3.1416}$$
$$\textbf{AREA SQ.IN.} = \textbf{CIRCUMFERENCE}^2 \textbf{ x .07958}$$

Example: What is the area of square inch of a #4 conductor that has a diameter of 0.232"?

.232 x .232 x .7854 = .042 area sq.in.

Example: What is the area of square inch of a #2 THHN conductor that has an approximate diameter of .388"?

.388 x .388 x .7854 = .1182 area sq.in.

328

Copper, 75°C Thermoplastic Insulated Cable Damage Table						
Copper Wire Size 75°C Thermoplastic	Maximum Short-Circuit Withstand Current in Amperes For					
	1/8 Cycle	1/4 Cycle	1/2 Cycle	1 Cycle	2 Cycles	3 Cycles
#14	4800	3400	2400	1700	1200	1000
#12	7600	5400	3800	2700	1900	1550
#10	12000	8500	6020	4300	3000	2450
#8	19200	13500	9600	6800	4800	3900
#6	30400	21500	15200	10800	7600	6200
#4	48400	34200	24200	17100	12100	9900

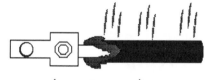

INSULATION DAMAGE

#6 THW can withstand
15,218 amps for 1/2 cycle

TERMINAL DAMAGE
(loosening of lugs)

#6 THW can withstand
22,090 amps for 1/2 cycle

MELTING

#6 THW can withstand
39,704 amps for 1/2 cycle

IF THE CURRENT CONTINUED
FOR 5 SECONDS (300 cycles)
THE #6 THW WOULD MELT AT
1620 AMPS

329

TYPICAL AMBIENT TEMPERATURES

LOCATION	TEMPERATURE	Minimum Rating of Insulation
Well ventilated, normally heated buildings	30°C (86°F)	* (see note below)
Buildings with such major heat sources as power stations or industrial processes	40°C (104°F)	75°C (167°F)
Poorly ventilated spaces such as attics	45°C (113°F)	75°C (167°F)
Furnaces and boiler rooms (minimum) (maximum)	40°C (104°F) 60°C (140°F)	75°C (167°F) 90°C (194°F)
Outdoors in the shade	40°C (104°F)	75°C (167°F)
In thermal insulation	45°C (113°F)	75°C (167°F)
Direct solar exposure	45°C (113°F)	75°C (167°F)
Places above 60°C (140°F)	-----	110°C (230°F)

*Note: 60°C for up to and including #8 copper and up to and including #6 aluminum. 75°C for over #8 copper and #6 aluminum.

MELTING POINT OF METALS

ALUMINUM	660°C - 1220°F
BRASS	900°C - 1652°F
BRONZE	1000°C - 1832°F
COPPER	1083°C - 1981°F
GOLD	1063°C - 1945°F
IRON	1400°C - 2552°F
LEAD	327°C - 621°F
SILVER	960°C - 1760°F
STAINLESS STEEL	1500°C - 2732°F

16 drams = 1 ounce
16 ounces = 1 pound
1 ton = 2000 pounds
1 U.S. pint = 16 fluid ounces
1 standard cup = 8 fluid ounces
1 tablespoon = .5 fluid ounces
1 teaspoon = .16 fluid ounces
2 pints = 1 quart
4 quarts = 1 gallon
1 U.S. gallon = .833 Imperial gallon
1 U.S. gallon = 3.785 liters
1 gallon = 8.24 pounds
12 inches = 1 foot
3 feet = 1 yard
5.5 yards = 1 rod
40 rods = 1 furlong
5280 feet = 1 mile
43,560 sq.ft. = 1 acre
640 acres = 1 square mile
1 square mile = 1 section
36 sections = 1 Township

RELATIONSHIP BETWEEN METRIC and ENGLISH

LENGTH	=	**metre (m)**
AREA	=	**square metre (m²)**
VOLUME	=	**cubic metre (m³)**

1 millimeter(mm) = .001 meter

1 centimeter(cm) = .01 meter

1 millimeter = 39.37 mils
.03937 inch

1 centimeter = .3937 inch
.0328 ft

1 meter = 1,000 millimeter(mm)
39.37 inch
3.281 feet

1 mil = .0254 mm
1 inch = 25.4 mm
2.54 cm
.0254 m

1 foot = 304.8 mm
30.48 cm
.3048 m

RELATIONSHIP BETWEEN METRIC and ENGLISH

1 mile   =   1.609 kilometers (km)

1 kilometer   =   .621 miles

miles x 1.6 = kilometers

kilometers/1.6 = miles

Example: 45 miles per hour is how many kilometers?
Solution: 45 mph x 1.6 = 72 km

Example: 64 kilometers is how many miles per hour?
Solution: 64km/1.6 = 40 mph

1 liter   =   .264178 gallon

1 gallon   =   3.785 liters

1 quart   =   .946 liters

1 pint   =   .473 liters

THERMOMETER SCALE
Centigrade - Fahrenheit

Centigrade = 5/9 (F-32)				Fahrenheit = 9/5 C + 32			
C	F	C	F	C	F	C	F
-35	-31.0	13	55.4	49	120.2	85	185.0
-30	-22.0	14	57.2	50	122.0	86	186.8
-25	-13.0	15	59.0	51	123.8	87	188.6
-20	-4.0	16	60.8	52	125.6	88	190.4
-19	-2.2	17	62.6	53	127.4	89	192.2
-18	-.4	18	64.4	54	129.2	90	194.0
-17	1.4	19	66.2	55	131.0	91	195.8
-16	3.2	20	68.0	56	132.8	92	197.6
-15	5.0	21	69.8	57	134.6	93	199.4
-14	6.8	22	71.6	58	136.4	94	201.2
-13	8.6	23	73.4	59	138.2	95	203.0
-12	10.4	24	75.2	60	140.0	96	204.8
-11	12.2	25	77.0	61	141.8	97	206.6
-10	14.0	26	78.8	62	143.6	98	208.4
-9	15.8	27	80.6	63	145.4	99	210.2
-8	17.6	28	82.4	64	147.2	100	212
-7	19.4	29	84.2	65	149.0	105	221
-6	21.2	30	86.0	66	150.8	110	230
-5	23.0	31	87.8	67	152.6	115	239
-4	24.8	32	89.6	68	154.4	120	248
-3	26.6	33	91.4	69	156.2	130	266
-2	28.4	34	93.2	70	158.0	140	284
-1	30.2	35	95.0	71	159.8	150	302
0	32.0	36	96.8	72	161.6	160	320
1	33.8	37	98.6	73	163.4	170	338
2	35.6	38	100.4	74	165.2	180	356
3	37.4	39	102.2	75	167.0	190	374
4	39.2	40	104.0	76	168.8	200	392
5	41.0	41	105.8	77	170.6	250	482
6	42.8	42	107.6	78	172.4	300	572
7	44.6	43	109.4	79	174.2	350	662
8	46.4	44	111.2	80	176.0	400	752
9	48.2	45	113.0	81	177.8	500	932
10	50.0	46	114.8	82	179.6	600	1112
11	51.8	47	116.0	83	181.4	800	1472
12	53.6	48	118.4	84	183.2	1000	1832

TEMPERATURE CONVERSION

Water boils at	100°C	212°F
Water freezes at	0°C	32°F
Difference of	100°	180°

The change Celsius is equivalent to 180/100 or 9/5 or 1.8° change on the Fahrenheit scale. A degree of change on the Fahrenheit scale is equivalent to 100/180 or 5/9 or .555° change on the Celsius scale.

The conversion formulas are:

(degrees F - 32) (5/9) = degrees Celsius

(degrees C) (9/5) + 32 = degrees Fahrenheit

Example: Convert 86°F to 30°C.

The formula shows the first step is to subtract 32° from 86° = 54°, multiply 54° x 5/9 = 270/9 = **30°C**.

Example: Convert 30°C to 86°F.

The formula shows the first step is to multiply 30°C x 9/5 = 270/5 = 54°, 54° + 32 = **86°F**.

Bolt size	Threads per inch	Drill bit for tap	Decimal Equivalent	Drill bit for clearance	Decimal Equivalent
1/8"	40	#38	.1015	#29	.1360
1/8"	44	#37	.1040	#29	.1360
#6	32	#36	.1065	#25	.1495
#6	40	#33	.1130	#25	.1495
#8	32	#29	.1360	#16	.1770
#8	36	#29	.1360	#16	.1770
#10	24	#25	.1495	13/64"	.2031
#10	32	#21	.1590	13/64"	.2031
#12	24	#16	.1770	7/32"	.2188
#12	28	#14	.1820	7/32"	.2188
1/4"	20	#7	.2010	17/64"	.2656
1/4"	28	#3	.2130	17/64"	.2656
5/16"	18	F	.2570	21/64"	.3281
5/16"	24	#1	.2720	21/64"	.3281
3/8"	16	5/16"	.3125	25/64"	.3906
3/8"	24	Q	.3320	25/64"	.3906
7/16"	14	U	.3680	29/64"	.4531
7/16"	20	25/64"	.3906	29/64"	.4531
1/2"	13	27/64"	.4219	33/64"	.5156
1/2"	20	29/64"	.4531	33/64"	.5156
9/16"	12	31/64"	.4844	37/64"	.5781
9/16"	18	33/64"	.5156	37/64"	.5781
5/8"	11	17/32"	.5312	41/64"	.6406
5/8"	18	37/64"	.5781	41/64"	.6406
3/4"	10	21/32"	.6562	49/64"	.7656
3/4"	16	11/16"	.6875	49/64"	.7656
7/8"	9	49/64"	.7656	57/64"	.8906
7/8"	14	13/16"	.8125	57/64"	.8906
1"	8	7/8"	.8750	1 1/64"	1.0156
1"	14	15/16"	.9375	1 1/64"	1.0156

APPROXIMATE DIMENSIONS OF CONDUIT FITTINGS

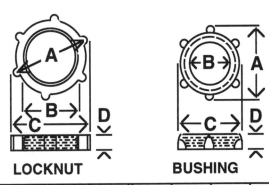

LOCKNUT   **BUSHING**

NOMINAL PIPE SIZE	A	B	C	D	A	B	C	D
$\frac{3}{8}$"	$1\frac{1}{16}$"	$\frac{5}{8}$"	1"	$\frac{1}{8}$"	$\frac{27}{32}$"	$\frac{15}{32}$"	$\frac{3}{4}$"	$\frac{5}{16}$"
$\frac{1}{2}$"	$1\frac{3}{32}$"	$\frac{25}{32}$"	$1\frac{1}{16}$"	$\frac{1}{8}$"	$1\frac{1}{32}$"	$\frac{5}{8}$"	$\frac{29}{32}$"	$\frac{11}{32}$"
$\frac{3}{4}$"	$1\frac{11}{32}$"	1"	$1\frac{9}{32}$"	$\frac{5}{32}$"	$1\frac{1}{4}$"	$\frac{3}{4}$"	$1\frac{5}{32}$"	$\frac{7}{16}$"
1"	$1\frac{21}{32}$"	$1\frac{1}{4}$"	$1\frac{19}{32}$"	$\frac{5}{32}$"	$1\frac{17}{32}$"	$1\frac{1}{32}$"	$1\frac{13}{32}$"	$\frac{9}{16}$"
$1\frac{1}{4}$"	$2\frac{1}{8}$"	$1\frac{19}{32}$"	$2\frac{1}{32}$"	$\frac{7}{32}$"	$1\frac{29}{32}$"	$1\frac{5}{16}$"	$1\frac{3}{4}$"	$\frac{9}{16}$"
$1\frac{1}{2}$"	$2\frac{3}{8}$"	$1\frac{13}{32}$"	$2\frac{1}{4}$"	$\frac{3}{16}$"	$2\frac{5}{32}$"	$1\frac{17}{32}$"	$2\frac{1}{32}$"	$\frac{5}{8}$"
2"	$2\frac{31}{32}$"	$2\frac{5}{16}$"	$2\frac{25}{32}$"	$\frac{7}{32}$"	$2\frac{25}{32}$"	2"	$2\frac{17}{32}$"	$\frac{19}{32}$"
$2\frac{1}{2}$"	$3\frac{17}{32}$"	$2\frac{3}{4}$"	$3\frac{5}{16}$"	$\frac{1}{4}$"	$3\frac{5}{8}$"	$2\frac{13}{32}$"	3"	$\frac{25}{32}$"
3"	$4\frac{5}{16}$"	$3\frac{3}{8}$"	$4\frac{1}{32}$"	$\frac{5}{16}$"	$3\frac{7}{8}$"	$3\frac{1}{32}$"	$3\frac{11}{16}$"	$\frac{27}{32}$"
$3\frac{1}{2}$"	5"	$3\frac{15}{16}$"	$4\frac{5}{8}$"	$\frac{5}{16}$"	$4\frac{17}{32}$"	$3\frac{15}{32}$"	$4\frac{9}{32}$"	$\frac{29}{32}$"
4"	$5\frac{3}{8}$"	$4\frac{7}{16}$"	$5\frac{3}{16}$"	$\frac{7}{16}$"	$5\frac{1}{8}$"	4"	$4\frac{25}{32}$"	$\frac{7}{8}$"
$4\frac{1}{2}$"	$6\frac{3}{32}$"	$4\frac{7}{8}$"	$5\frac{25}{32}$"	$\frac{1}{2}$"	$5\frac{3}{4}$"	$4\frac{15}{32}$"	$5\frac{7}{16}$"	$1\frac{1}{32}$"
5"	$6\frac{3}{4}$"	$5\frac{15}{32}$"	$6\frac{7}{16}$"	$\frac{9}{16}$"	$6\frac{3}{8}$"	$5\frac{1}{32}$"	$6\frac{1}{32}$"	$1\frac{1}{32}$"
6"	$7\frac{19}{32}$"	$6\frac{1}{2}$"	$7\frac{29}{32}$"	$\frac{5}{8}$"	$7\frac{13}{32}$"	$6\frac{1}{16}$"	$7\frac{5}{32}$"	$1\frac{1}{8}$"

SPLIT-PHASE MOTOR

CLOCKWISE

Split-phase motors 1/20 - 3/4 hp are used on appliances, furnaces, small pumps, etc.

The split-phase motor and the capacitor-start motor can be reversed by interchanging the start leads. If the start leads are not available, the run leads can be interchanged to reverse the motor.

The start winding is the "red" and "black" wires. One motor direction would have "red" connected to **1** and "black" connected to **2**. To reverse the rotation, the start windings are reversed by connecting "red" to **2** and "black" to **1**.

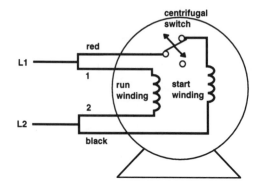

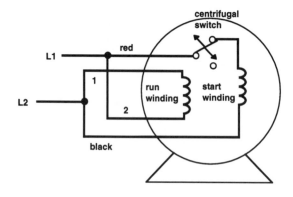

338

CAPACITOR-START MOTOR (single voltage)

Capacitor start motors are used for heavier loads up to 35 hp. They can be reversed by interchanging the start leads. If the start leads are not available, the run leads can be interchanged to reverse the motor.

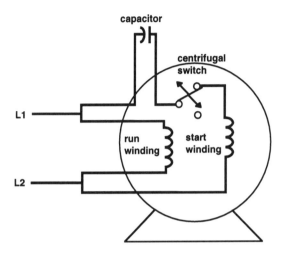

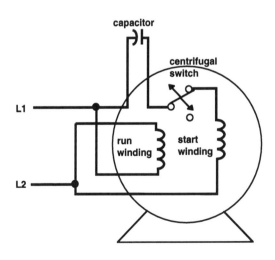

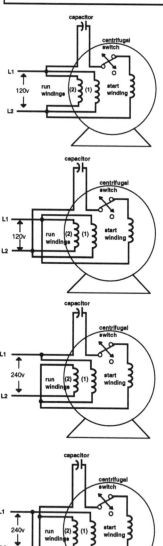

STANDARD ROTATION
FACING SHAFT END

CLOCKWISE

STANDARD ROTATION
FACING SHAFT END

COUNTER
CLOCKWISE

STANDARD ROTATION
FACING SHAFT END

CLOCKWISE

STANDARD ROTATION
FACING SHAFT END

COUNTER
CLOCKWISE

340

REPULSION MOTOR (wound-rotor)

The repulsion motor (wound-rotor) has brushes and a varying-speed characteristic. This motor is reversed by shifting the brushes 15 degrees.

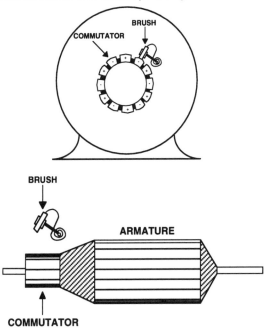

The repulsion-type motor is one of the oldest forms of single-phase induction motors. Since 1950 this motor has been largely replaced by the split-phase and capacitor-start induction motors.

D.C. MOTOR REVERSING

SERIES or SHUNT - Interchange the connections of either the field or the armature winding. Reversing the line leads will **not** change the direction of rotation.

COMPOUND - Interchange the connections of the two armature leads.

THREE-PHASE MOTOR

To reverse the direction of rotation with a three-phase motor, interchange any two motor leads or line wires.

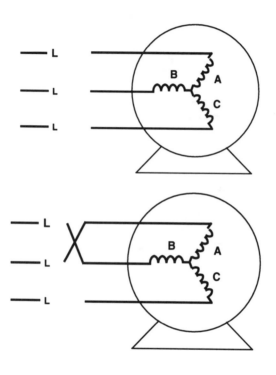

$3\emptyset \text{ va} = E \times I \times 1.732$

SYNCHRONOUS MOTOR

Synchronous motors vary in size to thousands of horsepower. It is an AC motor in which the rotor revolves in step or in synchronism with the rotating magnetic field produced by the stator winding. This means the magnetic field and the rotor turn at the same speed.

With the induction motor, the rotor turns at a lower speed than the revolving field. This is necessary in order that the squirrel-cage winding be cut by the revolving field and thereby have a current induced in it.

Slip is defined as the difference in speed between the rotor's actual rpm and that of the magnetic field. A synchronous motor has zero slip.

Synchronous motors are often used to improve the power factor of an electrical system. When used for power factor correction, the field windings are overexcited and cause the motor to draw a large leading current.

SYNCHRONOUS RPM =

$$\frac{HERTZ \times 120}{POLES}$$

TORQUE (LB-FT) =

$$\frac{Horsepower \times 5250}{RPM}$$

HORSEPOWER =

$$\frac{Torque\ (lb\text{-}ft) \times RPM}{5250}$$

343

ROTOR - STATOR

There are two types of motor rotors, the squirrel cage and the wound rotor. The squirrel cage has bars of copper or aluminum the length of the rotor electrically connected at each end with shorting rings. The wound rotor has coils of wires wound in the slots of the rotor.

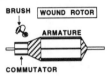

There must be a **motion** between the armature windings and the field windings. AC generators are built in two major assemblies, the **stator** and the **rotor**.

There are two types of motion, either the revolving armature (rotor) or the revolving field (stator).

In the **revolving armature** AC generator, the stator provides a stationary electromagnetic field. The rotor acting as the armature, revolves in the field, cutting the lines of force, producing the desired voltage. In this generator, the armature output is taken through slip rings and thus retains its AC characteristic.

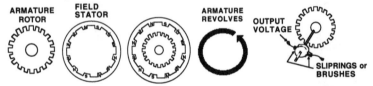

The **revolving field** AC generator is by far the most widely used today. In this type of generator, direct current from a separate source (excitation) is passed through windings on the rotor by means of sliprings and brushes. This maintains a rotating electromagnetic field of fixed polarity. The rotating magnetic field cuts through the armature windings embedded in the surrounding stator. As the rotor turns, AC voltages are induced in the windings since magnetic fields of first one polarity and then another cut through them. Now here is the important part; since the output power is taken from **stationary windings**, the output may be connected through **fixed** terminals and not revolving sliprings or brushes that would limit high voltages.

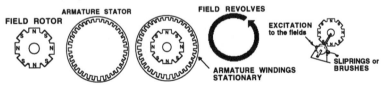

344

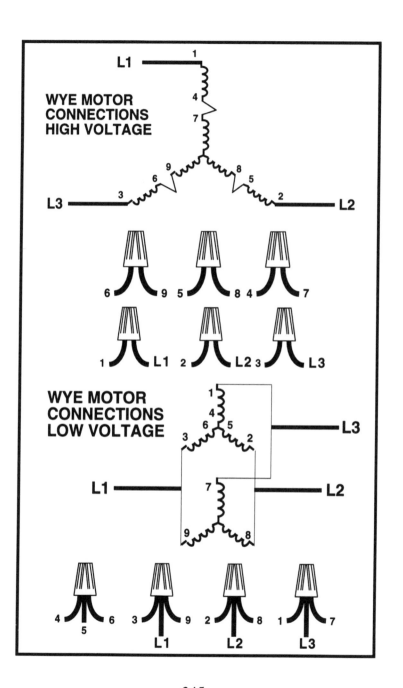

WYE MOTOR CONNECTIONS HIGH VOLTAGE

WYE MOTOR CONNECTIONS LOW VOLTAGE

345

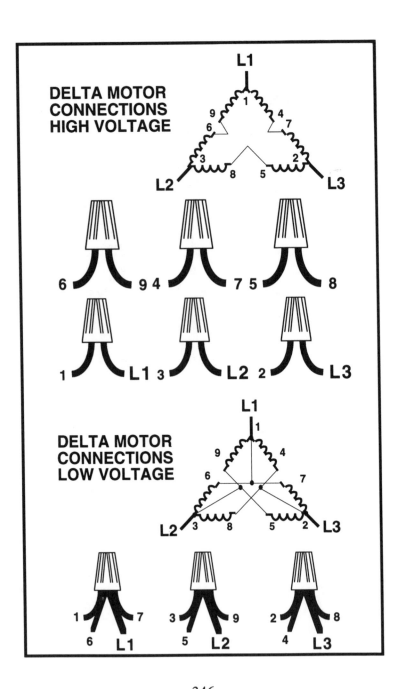

DELTA MOTOR CONNECTIONS HIGH VOLTAGE

DELTA MOTOR CONNECTIONS LOW VOLTAGE

346

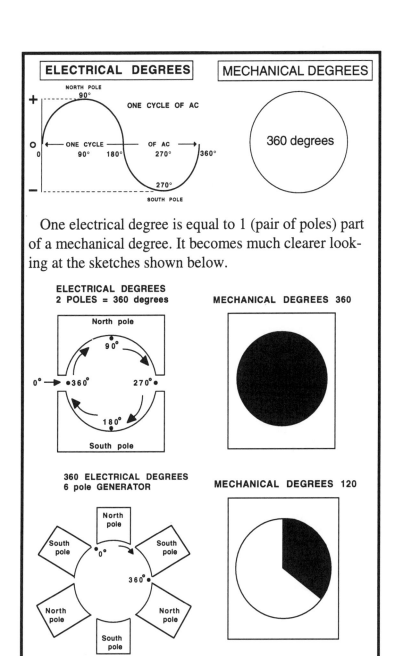

One electrical degree is equal to 1 (pair of poles) part of a mechanical degree. It becomes much clearer looking at the sketches shown below.

TRANSFORMER CONNECTIONS

A single phase transformer has one primary winding and one secondary winding. This is the simplest to connect. The high-voltage leads are marked "H" and the low voltage "X".

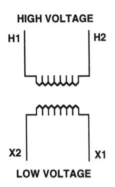

HIGH VOLTAGE

When facing the transformer low-voltage terminals H1 is to the left and H2 to the right. X1 is on the right, and X2 on the left.

LOW VOLTAGE

By **reversing** the 240 volts the transformer can be stepped up to 480 volts.

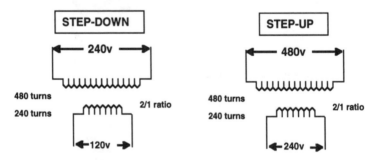

For a single low voltage of 120, the secondary windings are connected in **parallel**. "A" is connected to "C" and "B" is connected to "D". "A-C" connects to X2 and "B-D" to X1. Connection for **high-voltage** is made by connecting the windings in **series**. Voltages **add** in series.

348

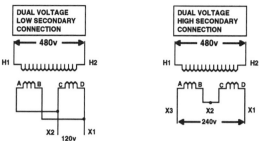

Transformers have a relative polarity which must be considered when connecting them. In a single phase transformer the voltage relationships are either "in phase" or 180° out of phase. Therefore, when the windings are connected together, the output voltage can either be **additive** or **subtractive**.

Batteries have polarities, if you connected one flashlight battery in reverse their voltages would cancel and the flashlight would not light.

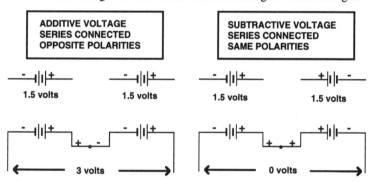

Although the voltages of a transformer are constantly changing, their relative phase angle to each other is constant. •Transformers under 200 kva with voltages ratings below 9000 volts will be additive.

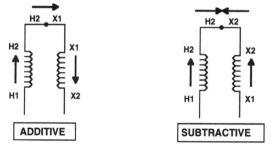

Most often transformers are manufactured with dual windings.

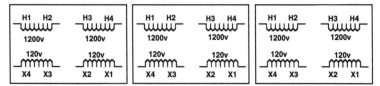

These transformers can be connected either wye for high voltage and low current, or delta for low voltage and high current.

Delta-Delta. With a 2400v source to the transformers, this is twice the 1200v rating of the primary windings. The 1200v primary windings must be connected in **series** for a 2400v source.

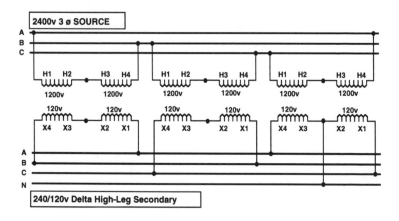

To provide the 240 volts, the 120v secondaries must be connected in **series**. Only one transformer in a Delta has a neutral connection which is grounded. From "A" or "C" phase to neutral would provide 240 volts. From "B" phase (high-leg) to neutral 208 volts.

350

AUTOTRANSFORMER

Where the desired voltage ratio is **less than two to one**, an autotransformer is often used.

An **autotransformer** makes common use of a part of a **single** winding for both the primary and secondary. The secondary load is simply transferred rather than transformed.

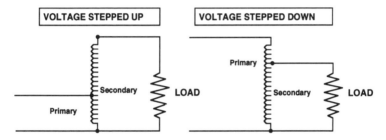

A common application of an autotransformer is a "buck" or "boost" transformer. Because transformers have a relative polarity, they can be wired so the secondary voltage either adds or subtracts. When the voltage adds, it is a "boost" transformer. When it subtracts it is called a "buck".

Shown below is the connection of a boost transformer with dual-primary and dual-secondary windings with a 10/1 ratio raising the 208v to 228.8 volts.

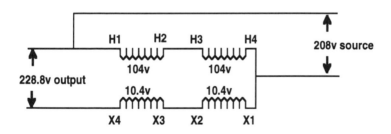

CURRENT TRANSFORMER (CT) (Doughnut)

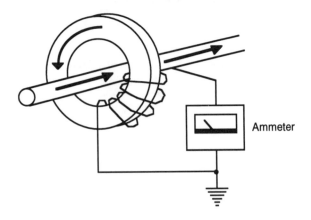

Ammeter

A current transformer is used when AC current is so large that connecting measuring instruments such as a kwh meter would be impracticable. The CT provides a means of reproducing the effect of the primary current on a **reduced scale** suited to the kwh meter.

To standardize current devices the *secondary* of a current transformer is always *rated* at **5 amperes,** no matter what the ampere rating of the primary is.

The current *rating* of the primary is determined by the maximum load current to be measured.

Example: Maximum load current to be measured is 500 amperes. The secondary winding will have a *rating* of 5 amperes. The ratio between the primary winding and the secondary winding is 5/500 = 1 to 100.

Thus, the secondary winding will have 100 times as many turns as the primary.

Using this 1/100 ratio, a current transformer for a load of 400 amps, the secondary would read 4 amps. For a load current of 300 amps the secondary would read 3 amps.

With the doughnut type (CT), the conductor passing through the center magnetizes the core because of magnetic lines around the single (one turn) conductor. The secondary has many turns of small wire connected directly to a low-scale ammeter.

VOLTAGE POTENTIAL TRANSFORMER

Usually circuits up to 600 volts can be measured directly with meters. However, higher voltages cause the meters to become very expensive in cost.

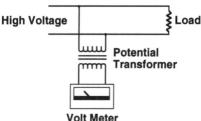

High Voltage — **Load**

Potential Transformer

Volt Meter

The potential transformer is used in metering of higher voltages. The primary winding is connected to the high-voltage and the secondary low-voltage winding usually wound for 120 volts.

The capacity of a potential transformer is relatively small as compared to a *power* transformer.

Potential transformers have ratings of 100 to 500 va.

PARALLEL WIRING TRANSFORMERS

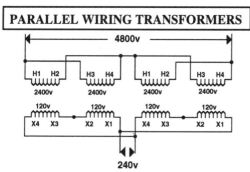

4800v

| H1 H2 | H3 H4 | H1 H2 | H3 H4 |
| 2400v | 2400v | 2400v | 2400v |

| 120v | 120v | 120v | 120v |
| X4 X3 | X2 X1 | X4 X3 | X2 X1 |

240v

To drop 2400 volts across each primary winding from the 4800 volts impressed by the source, each **pair of windings** will need to be connected in **series.** H2 is connected of one transformer is connected to H3 of the second transformer, and H4 on the first transformer is connected to H1 of the second transformer. Next the two transformers are connected in **parallel** and attached to the source of 4800v.

To obtain 240 volts on the secondary, X2 and X3 of each transformer is connected in **series.** Next these two sets of windings are connected in **parallel** and attached to the 240v load.

353

THE OPEN DELTA

It is possible to achieve three-phase by using only two transformers. This connection is called the *open delta* or *V-connection.*

Although the open-delta is generally used only as an emergency or temporary system, an original transformer installation may consist of an open-delta bank to supply a three-phase load which is presently light but is expected to increase in the future. This keeps the initial cost low by using only two transformers, a third transformer can be added to the system later when the demand requires it. When the third transformer is added, a delta-delta **closed** bank is formed.

A three-phase transformer with an assembly of three separate single-phase transformers in one tank is lower in initial cost, costs less to install, and requires less space than three separate single-phase transformers.

A three-phase transformer has one disadvantage if one of the phase windings becomes defective, the entire three-phase bank must be disconnected and removed from service. A defective single-phase transformer in a three-phase bank can be disconnected and removed for repair. Partial service can be restored using the remaining single phase transformers open-delta until a replacement transformer is obtained. With two transformers three-phase is still obtained, but at reduced power; **57.7%** of original power.

This makes it a very practical transformer application for temporary or emergency conditions.

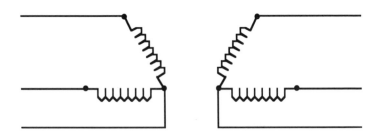

OPEN-DELTA 57.7%

GENERAL CONVERSION TABLE

British Thermal Units x 777.5 = foot-pounds
British Thermal Units x 3.93 ÷ 10,000 = horsepower hours
British Thermal Units x 2.93 ÷ 10,000 = Kilowatt hours
B. T. Us. per minute x 13.0 = foot pounds per second
B. T. Us. per minute x 1.76 ÷ 100 = Kilowatts
B. T. Us. per hour x 2.93 ÷ 10,000 = Kilowatts
B. T. Us. per hour x 2.98 ÷ 1,000,000 = Boiler horsepower
Circular Mils x 0.7854 = Square Mils
Cubic feet per minute x 7.48 = U. S. Gals. per minute
Cubic feet per minute x 6.23 = Imperial gals. per minute
Degrees x 0.01745 = Radians
Feet x 30.5 = Centimeters
Feet x 0.305 = Meters
Feet of Water x 0.883 = Inches of Mercury
Feet of Water x 62.43 = Pounds per square foot
Feet of Water x 0.43135 = Pounds per square inch
Feet per minute x 1.36 ÷ 100 = Miles per hour
Feet per second x 0.682 = Miles per hour
Foot pounds x 2.29 ÷ 1000 = British Thermal Units
Foot pounds x 5.05 ÷ 10,000,000 = Horsepower hours
Foot pounds x 3.77 ÷ 10,000,000 = Kilowatt hours
Foot pounds per minute x 1.29 ÷ 1000 = B. T. Us. per minute
Foot pounds per minute x 3.03 ÷ 100,000 = Horsepower
Foot pounds per second x 1.82 ÷ 1000 = Horsepower
Gallons U. S. x 0.134 = Cubic feet
Gallons Imperial x 0.160 = Cubic feet
Gallons U. S. x 0.833 = Imperial Gals.
Gallons Imperial x 1.2 = U. S. Gals.
Horsepower x 42.4 = B. T. Us. per minute
Horsepower x 33,000 = Foot pounds per minute
Horsepower x 550 = Foot pounds per second
Horsepower x 0.746 = Kilowatt
Horsepower Boiler x 33520 = B. T. Us. per hour
Horsepower Boiler x 9.80 = Kilowatts
Horsepower hours x 2550 = British Thermal Units
Horsepower hours x 1,980,000 = Foot pounds
Inches of mercury x 1.133 = Feet of water
Inches of mercury x 70.7 = Pounds per square foot
Inches of mercury x 0.491 = Pounds per square inch
Inches of water x 0.0735 = Inches of mercury
Inches of water x 5.20 = Pounds per square foot
Kilowatts x 56.9 = B. T. Us. per minute
Kilowatts x 3412 = B. T. Us. per hour
Kilowatts x 1.341 = Horsepower
Kilowatt hours x 3412 = British Thermal Units
Kilowatt hours x 1.34 = Horsepower hours
Miles per hour x 1.47 = Feet per second
Minutes x 2.91 ÷ 10,000 = Radians
Pounds per square foot x 1.60 ÷ 100 = Feet of water
Pounds per square inch x 2.31 = Feet of water
Pounds per square inch x 144 = Pounds per square foot
Radians x 57.3 = Degrees
Radians x 3438 = Minutes
Revolutions x 6.28 = Radians
Revolutions per Min. x 0.105 = Radians per second
Square inch x 273, 000 = Circular Mils